BIOLOGY OF BIRDS

The Natural History Press, publisher for The American Museum of Natural History, is a division of Doubleday & Company, Inc. Directed by a joint editorial board made up of members of the staff of both the Museum and Doubleday, the Natural History Press publishes books and periodicals in all branches of the life and earth sciences, including anthropology and astronomy. The Natural History Press has its editorial offices at The American Museum of Natural History, Central Park West at 79th Street, New York 24, New York, and its business offices at 501 Franklin Avenue, Garden City, New York.

WESLEY E. LANYON, Associate Curator in the Department of Ornithology at The American Museum of Natural History, was born in Norwalk, Connecticut on June 10, 1926. He received his A.B. from Cornell University in 1950 and his Ph.D. from the University of Wisconsin in 1955.

Dr. Lanyon joined the staff of The American Museum of Natural History in 1957. Previous to this, he taught at the University of Arizona and at Miami University in Ohio. His field work has included five summers with the National Park Service and field studies in Wisconsin and other north central states, in Mexico and Central America, the West Indies, and at The American Museum's Southwestern Research Station at Portal, Arizona.

Articles by Dr. Lanyon have appeared in many publications, including *Ecology, The Auk,* and *Condor*. He is a member of the American Ornithologists' Union, the Cooper Ornithological Society, the Wilson Ornithological Society, the Society of Systematic Zoology, the Society for the Study of Evolution, the Eastern Bird Banding Association, the Ecological Society of America, and Sigma Xi.

Dr. Lanyon and his wife and two children live at the Kalbfleisch Field Research Station of The American Museum of Natural History in Huntington, Long Island, where he is the Resident Director.

BIOLOGY OF
BIRDS

Wesley E. Lanyon

ASSOCIATE CURATOR,
DEPARTMENT OF ORNITHOLOGY
THE AMERICAN MUSEUM OF NATURAL HISTORY

Published for
The American Museum of Natural History

The Natural History Press

GARDEN CITY, NEW YORK

1964

All illustrations for this book were prepared by the Graphic Arts Division
of The American Museum of Natural History, many from exhibit material
in The Biology of Birds (Sanford Memorial) Hall at the Museum.

BIOLOGY OF BIRDS was originally published by the Natural History Press
in an American Museum Science Books paperback edition.

PREFACE

Birds hold a great fascination and appeal for many people, perhaps to a greater degree than any other group of animals. Many popular books appear annually that help us to identify birds, to attract them to our homes, and to learn about interesting birds of other lands. It is only natural that these pursuits should generate a deeper curiosity about the more basic aspects of the biology of birds. We at The American Museum of Natural History are constantly requested to answer such questions as: What is known of the origin of birds and their relationships with other animals? Why are birds found where they are? How and why do birds migrate? How do birds care for their young? It is in response to the need for an inexpensive, non-technical presentation of the principles of avian biology that this book has been written. It can scarcely qualify as a textbook in ornithology, for the low cost and reduced format preclude a comprehensive treatment of the subject. Nevertheless, an effort has been made to provide the lay reader with the basis for an understanding of the principles of avian biology and for an appreciation of the great diversity of structure and behavior among birds. Hopefully, the reader will be stimulated to seek additional information in the authoritative references presented in the appendix.

In preparing this book I have drawn freely from the exhibit materials located within the Sanford Hall of the Biology of Birds at The American Museum of Natural History. To my colleagues and predecessors in the Department of Ornithology who supervised the preparation of these exhibits, and to the artists of the Graphic Arts Division who prepared the figures, I am deeply indebted.

New York City   Wesley E. Lanyon
May 1963

CONTENTS

LIST OF ILLUSTRATIONS

BIOLOGY OF BIRDS

1 ORIGIN AND EVOLUTION

A strange bird-like creature the size of a crow glided out over the shallow lagoon of a Bavarian lake. Or was it more reptile-like? We cannot be sure for it appeared to have some of the features of both reptiles and birds. A group of dinosaurs browsed on the shrubbery along the shore, and large flying reptiles were flapping their leathery wings and circling overhead. Suddenly our bird-like creature, with its feeble powers of flight, was unable to cope with a sharp gust of wind and fell into the shallow waters below and drowned. Sediments buried it and these were subsequently turned to stone. One hundred and forty million years later, men were working in the slate deposits formed from the sediments of this same Bavarian lake and chanced upon the fossil impression left by this creature. Thus came about the discovery of what scientists consider to be the oldest known bird and which they appropriately named *Archaeopteryx*, meaning "ancient wing."

The Oldest Known Bird

Strange as this ancient creature may appear to us now, it nevertheless had the essential characteristics that distinguish our modern birds from all other animals. Its bony backbone relates it to other vertebrate animals, including the fishes, amphibians, reptiles, and mammals, as distinct from the invertebrates such as starfish, insects, and earthworms. The fact that the flight surfaces of its wings and tail were composed of feathers rather than a membrane is of particular significance, for this characteristic separates it from all other vertebrates and especially from those specialized forms that had independently evolved the ability of true flight—ancient flying reptiles, and bats.

Just as we have already speculated upon the circumstances of its fortuitous drowning, a certain amount of educated guess-work has been necessary to reconstruct how this ancestral bird must have looked and behaved (Fig. 1). There is no doubt that *Archaeopteryx* was feathered. Indeed, this constitutes the

Fig. 1. *The oldest known bird,* Archaeopteryx. *A perfect link between reptiles and modern birds. Above, a reconstruction of how it looked, based on the fossil remains, below.*

strongest argument that it was a bird, for birds alone in the animal kingdom have developed feathers. Nearly all of the skeletal features of *Archaeopteryx*, however, were more like those of reptiles, including the long bony tail, clawed wings, toothed jaws, and comparatively heavy bones. These reptilian characteristics, of course, suggest the logical theory that birds arose from the reptiles. But the exact manner in which the change from reptile to bird took place is unfortunately largely a matter of deduction. We have no fossil record to help us with the details of this transformation. But paleontologists, scientists who make a study of fossils, assure us that there were reptiles having the potential characteristics for this change and that these could logically have been the forerunners of the first true birds.

In the search for the reptilian ancestor of *Archaeopteryx*, scientists point to primitive forms which may also have given rise to the dinosaurs and to the pterosaurs or flying reptiles. This ancestral form shifted its habits from a terrestrial way of life to an arboreal existence, possibly due to overcrowding among the increasing number of ground-dwelling dinosaurs that were destined to become the dominant animals of this period of geological time. But such a change in habits necessitated accompanying changes in anatomy and physiology as well (Fig. 2). Arboreal life opened up new possibilities for food supplies that may in turn have led to a reduction of teeth and jaw musculature. Longer feet and hands were required, along with an ability for grasping and perching. A heavy tail was no longer needed to balance the bipedal posture of the primitive ground reptile. Prior to these structural changes, there may have been an increase in the internal temperature of the body, over that of other reptiles, and an ability to maintain this warm-blooded condition independent of changes in the temperature of the surrounding air, thus permitting an acceleration of all bodily functions. Warm-bloodedness, or homoiothermy, is characteristic of only two major groups, birds and mammals, while all remaining animals are cold-blooded (poikilothermic). Even earlier reptiles, some of which gave rise to the mammals, may have already developed the potentialities of a warm-blooded circulation. The flying reptiles known as pterosaurs, for example, may have been at least partially warm-blooded and, unlike *Archaeopteryx*, had light, air-filled (pneumatic) bones as well. But the pterosaurs depended upon a membrane of skin for flight, as do bats, rather than upon feathers and are not thought to have been part of the direct line of descent of birds.

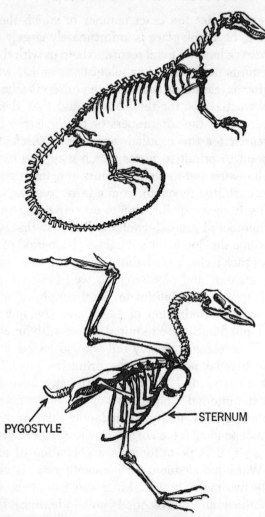

PYGOSTYLE

STERNUM

Fig. 2. Structural changes from reptile to bird. Note in particular the forelimb, in which the bones are lengthened, the first and fifth digits lost, and the claws reduced or lost; the strengthened breastbone (sternum) with its keel to support flight muscles; the shorter and stiffer rib cage (thorax); the tail, in which the number of vertebrae is reduced, the terminal ones being fused to form a pygostyle on which tail feathers are anchored.

Although the feather is considered a modified scale, the process of its transformation is still unknown. Possibly it came about in response to the warmer body temperatures. Feathers would certainly have had survival value in terms of the retention of this body heat and as insulation against the coolness of the new arboreal environment. In any event, the development of warm-bloodedness and of feathers almost certainly preceded the development of true flight in the first bird-like reptiles. That *Archaeopteryx* was not a particularly strong flier is surmised from the inadequacy of its skeleton for the support of the essential flight muscles. No doubt a gliding or passive type of flight preceded a flapping flight, the latter type awaiting the later modification of still further aspects of the skeleton (Fig. 3).

The Process of Evolution

Having established the identity of the oldest known bird and postulated a logical origin for it and all birds, there remains the problem of tracing the pattern of changes that have taken place in the history of birds between the time of *Archaeopteryx* and the present. These gradual changes, inherited through successive generations, collectively constitute a process known as evolution.

The evidence in support of the theory of evolution, provided from many different scientific disciplines, is now so overwhelmingly conclusive that few well-informed people doubt its validity. Our most important clues in unraveling the mysteries of the evolution of birds, as in that of any group of living organisms, are those available in the fossil record. But in addition to fossil remains, like those of *Archaeopteryx* in Bavaria, we must have a means of reckoning time down through the millions of years spanned by the fossil record. Fortunately there are "clocks" in the earth's crust that can give us this record of time. Radioactive elements such as uranium disintegrate at a slow, uniform rate over millions of years. Knowing this rate of decay and the rel-

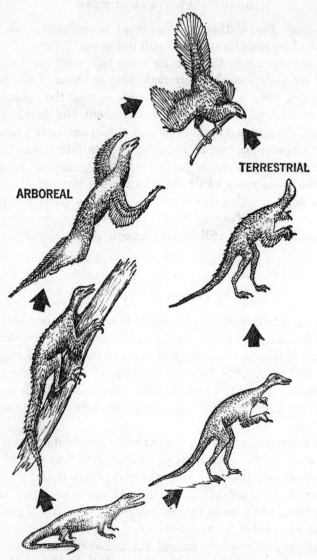

TERRESTRIAL

ARBOREAL

Fig. 3. *The origin of flight. According to one theory, the avian ancestors were terrestrial, dinosaur-like reptiles which used their "wings" to increase their running speed. On the other hand, pro avians may have lived in trees and used their "wings" for gliding to lengthen their jumps from branch to branch.*

ative proportions of the original element and the product of its decay, it then becomes possible to estimate the age of fossil-bearing rock. By reading these geological time clocks, together with the fossils that have been found, scientists have been able to approximate the dates of the origin and evolution of living things.

For convenience in discussing evolution, the entire history of the earth has been divided into a time scale composed of eras, periods, and epochs (Fig. 4). According to the geological time clock, *Archaeopteryx* lived in the Upper Jurassic period of the Mesozoic era, some one hundred and forty million years ago. Most of us have difficulty comprehending time in terms of millions of years. We need a more familiar "yardstick" for measuring evolutionary events, such as perhaps the airline distance between well-known points in the United States. Suppose that we were to let the distance between San Francisco and New York represent the full scale of geologic time, some two billion years, with The American Museum of Natural History in New York designating the present-day terminus of this "evolutionary journey." We then discover the amazing fact that we have no positive evidence of living organisms west of the Mississippi River on our yardstick of geologic time. Fossils of vertebrate animals extend westward as far as Chicago (Upper Cambrian, 500 million years ago), while birds have been on this evolutionary journey only since Harrisburg, Pennsylvania (Upper Jurassic). In terms of the age of the earth, the time spanned by the evolutionary development of birds may seem to be short indeed. Yet when we realize that the oldest human fossils date back only as far as Newark, New Jersey, on this imaginary journey of ours, we can perhaps better appreciate the considerable period of time that has elapsed since the days of *Archaeopteryx*.

The fossil record available for the reconstruction of the evolution of birds is woefully incomplete when compared with that of other vertebrate groups. Few complete fossilized bird skeletons have ever been found, and it is not difficult to understand the reasons for this. The bones of birds are fragile and rapidly de-

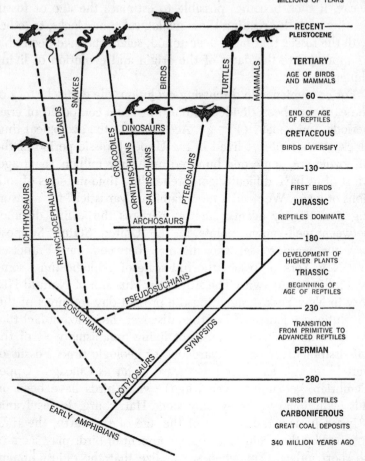

AGES SHOWN IN
MILLIONS OF YEARS

RECENT
PLEISTOCENE

TERTIARY

AGE OF BIRDS
AND MAMMALS

— 60 —

END OF AGE
OF REPTILES

CRETACEOUS

BIRDS DIVERSIFY

— 130 —

FIRST BIRDS

JURASSIC

REPTILES DOMINATE

— 180 —

DEVELOPMENT OF
HIGHER PLANTS

TRIASSIC

BEGINNING OF
AGE OF REPTILES

— 230 —

TRANSITION
FROM PRIMITIVE TO
ADVANCED REPTILES

PERMIAN

— 280 —

FIRST REPTILES

CARBONIFEROUS

GREAT COAL DEPOSITS

340 MILLION YEARS AGO

ICHTHYOSAURS
RHYNCHOCEPHALIANS
LIZARDS
SNAKES
CROCODILES
DINOSAURS
ORNITHISCHIANS
SAURISCHIANS
PTEROSAURS
BIRDS
TURTLES
MAMMALS
ARCHOSAURS
PSEUDOSUCHIANS
EOSUCHIANS
SYNAPSIDS
COTYLOSAURS
EARLY AMPHIBIANS

Fig. 4. Anatomical and physiological evidence, as well as fossils, indicates that birds are an offshoot of the large and varied class of reptiles. Strangely, few people would suspect that the closest living relatives of the birds are crocodiles. The dinosaurs, pterosaurs, and other orders of reptiles, which together with the avian ancestors formed the subclass of Archosaurs, are now extinct. Birds probably branched off the reptilian stem (Pseudosuchia) during the Triassic, although no fossils are known older than the upper Jurassic Archaeopteryx (140 million years ago).

composed, and the conditions essential for their preservation are seldom achieved. In view of the fantastic odds against the successful preservation of a bird's skeleton, we must regard the discovery of any fossil or impression as an extremely happy and fortunate accident. Likewise, it would be naïve for us to assume that the accidental drowning of *Archaeopteryx*, as postulated above, marked the beginning of the evolution of birds. It seems probable that similar and possibly other kinds of primitive reptile-like birds had already existed for some millions of years.

Patterns of Evolution

There is a gap of over thirty million years between the age of *Archaeopteryx* and that of the next oldest birds represented in the fossil record. The best documented of these Cretaceous birds was *Hesperornis* or "western bird," known from fossils discovered in chalk beds of Kansas. This was a flightless creature with some resemblance to a loon and, apparently, equally adept at diving and swimming as that modern bird. Though *Hesperornis* was toothed like *Archaeopteryx*, its vestigial wing suggests a rather long period of evolution and specialization since that primitive form. The second best-known bird of Cretaceous times has been named *Ichthyornis* or "fish bird," because of the shape of its vertebrae. It was apparently a good flier and about the size and shape of a gull. We cannot be certain, from the fossil evidence available, whether or not *Ichthyornis* had teeth. That these two birds of former inland seas were so remarkably different in structure suggests the possibility that considerable variation may have existed among birds in general by this point in geologic time, in spite of the lack of supporting fossil material.

Most of the modern groups of birds are well represented by fossils that have been taken from early Tertiary rock, or that point in geologic time corresponding to the Delaware River on our imaginary journey. Not having adequate fossil material from the Cretaceous means that it is impossible to reconstruct with certainty the relationships of these groups or to date their origin. The apparent evolution of this great variety of birdlife during the Cretaceous and early Tertiary has been correlated with the rise of true flowering plants. These plants, which are now the dominant forms within the plant kingdom, appear with relative suddenness and in great abundance at this point in the fossil record. By the late Cretaceous period, for example, the forests of North America were much like those of today, giving birds a great variety of food, nesting sites, and opportunities for shelter. Furthermore, the great numbers of flying reptiles had all but disappeared by the end of the Cretaceous, thus minimizing that possible source of competition.

While the early Tertiary was a period of rapid evolution of modern birds, it was likewise a period marked by the extinction of other groups. One such end point in evolutionary development was a bird that stood nearly seven feet tall, known as *Diatryma* (Fig. 5). Fossils of this flightless giant have been found from lower Tertiary deposits in a number of North American sites. One can imagine this giant terrestrial bird feeding upon carrion in the manner of vultures today, with the massive bill being used for crushing bones and flesh. In *Hesperornis* and *Diatryma* we have two highly specialized and structurally different birds, representing two different geologic periods. Both were confined to a flightless existence, the one in the sea and the other on land.

The origin and evolution of those birds that lack the appropriate structures and accompanying power for flight is of major concern to scientists. There are those who believe that all flightless birds, including the highly specialized penguins and Ostriches of today, represent a distinct line of evolution that diverged from the main stem of flying forms prior to the days of *Archaeopteryx*. In that event, the common ancestor for these flightless birds would have been an ancient, non-flying reptile-like form. There seems to be no logical reason, however, for supposing that all flightless birds had a common ancestry or, for that matter, that flightless birds must have evolved exclusively from flightless ancestors. A terrestrial vulture, known from early

Fig. 5. Reconstructions of Diatryma *(left) and* Hesperornis *swimming (right).*

Tertiary deposits in Wyoming, was quite unlike any of its living relatives, today, in having only a limited capacity for flight. Had it continued in its trend toward specialization for a terrestrial way of life, it too might have become flightless. Or it may indeed have become flightless, though no such fossil evidence has been found. Even though the earliest fossil penguins (of mid-Tertiary age) were already flightless, most workers today consider them to be descendants from a group of oceanic birds, such as the diving petrels, whose present-day members are capable of flight but who also use their wings in swimming. Likewise the Ostriches, rheas, and other flightless birds of the southern continents could conceivably have possessed the power of flight initially, but then lost it secondarily in favor of a swift-running type of locomotion. Their large size and powerful legs are characteristics associated with their loss of flight and are not necessarily indicative of a common ancestry.

Hesperornis, rather than constituting a link in a long chain of non-flying birds, may well have been an overspecialized derivative of the same ancestral form that also gave rise to our modern diving birds like the grebes and loons which possess the capacity for flight.

The fossil remains for a few of our living birds from deposits of late Tertiary times have led to the speculation that most of the present-day species of birds may have been present by the beginning of Pleistocene time, roughly one million years ago. While the pre-Pleistocene period was characterized by this rapid development of a host of new species, many of them modern, the Pleistocene and subsequent years down to historic time have been marked by the mass extinction of many forms, and by negligible structural changes in the remaining forms. All this points to a much richer bird fauna, in terms of variety of species, during the late Tertiary than that which we see about us today.

A distinctly subtropical climate throughout temperate North America until the late Tertiary would have favored this rapid evolution of new forms. This was followed by a cooling-off period, culminating in the southward advance of the glaciers during Pleistocene or the Ice Age. Geologists tell us that there were four periods of glaciation during the past million years, with extensive intervening or interglacial periods of warm climate comparable to our own today. The most recent recession of the ice sheet occurred no more than 10,000 years ago. Conditions during the Pleistocene were especially favorable for the preservation of fossil birds, and extensive collections have been made in North America, notably from asphalt pits in California, desert lake beds in Oregon and Kansas, and caves and streams in Florida.

Among the strangest of Pleistocene birds was a large vulture, *Teratornis* or "monstrous bird," known from deposits in California and Florida. Paleontologists estimate that it weighed twice that of our living California Condor and had a wing span of 12 feet. But a single bone uncovered from a Nevada cave is evidence of a still larger condor, nearly twice the size of

Teratornis and apparently the largest flying bird yet known. Extinct flamingos were once part of the bird life of Oregon, California, and South Dakota, and condors ranged eastward to Florida during this period. Crane-like birds, known from remains found in the northern Great Plains region, have since disappeared.

Each of the periods of geologic time has been marked by the disappearance of some of its most characteristic and abundant types of birds. Man, a product of evolution himself, has more than a casual interest in the causes of such extinctions. In some instances at least, they have been attributed to overspecialization for a restricted way of life, perhaps involving limitations of means of locomotion or of methods of obtaining food. These highly specialized birds would then be unable to cope with changes that might occur in their environment, such as marked

Fig. 6. Reconstruction of a moa.

shifts in the climate and the resulting modifications of the vegetation. No doubt the effects of competition from other birds perhaps better adapted for these changes or better capable of adjusting to them has been a significant factor as well. The non-flying aquatic forms like *Hesperornis*, for example, would certainly have been at a disadvantage when the inland seas dried up.

Some of the largest birds in the fossil record were apparently able to postpone their inevitable extinction until very recent times because of the comparatively sheltered existence they led on islands. The so-called elephant birds of Madagascar, *Aepyornis* or "tall bird," laid the largest eggs known, each with a capacity of over two gallons. They were massive, flightless birds that became extinct only after man came upon the scene. Their counterparts in New Zealand were the giant moas, *Dinornis* or "fearful birds," fossils of which date back to the late Tertiary. The largest of the moas must have been ten feet tall and weighed nearly 500 pounds (Fig. 6). The final extermination of these flightless giants, like that of the elephant birds, has been attributed to man, possibly as recently as the tenth or eleventh century. The Dodo (*Raphus*) was an extraordinarily large pigeon that lived only on the small island of Mauritius in the Indian Ocean. Its large size and inability to fly were not serious handicaps until man arrived and released pigs on the island some 300 years ago. The expression "dead as a dodo" is only too well known.

Fig. 7. Reconstruction of the Dodo.

2 DESIGN FOR FLIGHT

Flight is the most characteristic attribute of birds and has played a dominant role in their evolution. Long before his mastery of the air at Kitty Hawk, man had marveled at the wondrous spectacle of birds in flight. In spite of today's technological progress in the design and control of "flying machines" and the imminence of man's travel through outer space, birds remain without peers in the realm of true flight.

The development of flight in birds depended upon a solution to the seemingly conflicting demands of economy of weight and rigidity and strength of structure. Consequently, the distinctive features of the anatomy and physiology of birds, as compared with structures and processes among other animals, are those associated with flight and with the related high rate of body metabolism. There were additional demands placed upon the functional efficiency of various organ systems.

Feathers

Among the many engineering accomplishments that birds have achieved, the development and muscular control of feathers stands out as one of the major keys to their success. No other animals possess these remarkable structures. Feathers are both light and flexible and can be controlled with precision and agility. Yet each feather possesses the strength required for the stresses imposed by flight, there being no stronger substance of equivalent size and weight in nature. Feathers provide smooth and streamlined body contours which are essential for reduction of air friction and turbulence and, when properly groomed, are completely waterproof. They form one of the most efficient types of insulation known, because of the profusion of dead air spaces that they enclose, and thereby aid in maintaining the bird's high body temperature. Feathers also play important roles in courtship and sex recognition, but these particular functions will be considered in Chapters 3 and 6.

Although most birds appear to be uniformly covered with feathers, these structures normally arise only from certain rather well-defined regions or feather tracts, separated by patches of nearly naked skin (Fig. 8). Each feather tract con-

Fig. 8. Feather tracts and patches of naked skin illustrated here by a nestling Robin.

sists of hundreds of tiny pockets in the skin, known as follicles, from which the feathers emerge. At the base of each feather follicle there is a highly specialized group of cells or papilla which develops early in the bird's life and is responsible for the production of many successive generations of feathers. Each papilla consists of a core of cells from the inner layer of skin, the dermis, and a thin covering of cells from the outer layer or epidermis. All parts of the feather are derived from the epidermal component of this papilla, while the dermal cells provide the essential nourishment and pigments for the growing feather. Unlike the nails and hair of mammals, feathers do not grow continuously. Following a rapid growth to full size, the nutrient supply is cut off and the feather remains in the follicle as a dead structure. In the event of loss of the feather, either through a natural process of molt or through accident, dormant cells of the papilla are then stimulated to regenerate a replacement (Fig. 9).

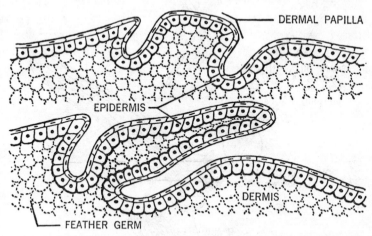

Fig. 9. *Development of a contour feather (early stages).*

The first generation of feathers to appear in each bird consists of the simplest and most uniform of all feather types, known as down. These soft, fluffy feathers may form a thick downy covering as in young waterfowl or be nearly absent as evidenced by the naked young of song birds. In either extreme, the down feathers are soon pushed from their follicles by the next generation of feathers, to which they remain attached until worn away. The incoming juvenile feathers are nearly fully developed by the time the young of many birds leave their nest, giving them the power of flight at that time or soon thereafter.

Most of the exposed body feathers of adult birds, including the stronger flight feathers of the wing and tail, are known as contour feathers. Each of these consists of a central shaft and an outer and inner vane made up of barbs and interlocking barbules and barbicels (Fig. 10). Hooklets (hamuli) of microscopic size, projecting from the barbicels, hold the parts of the vane together in a continuous, unbroken sheet. In the event

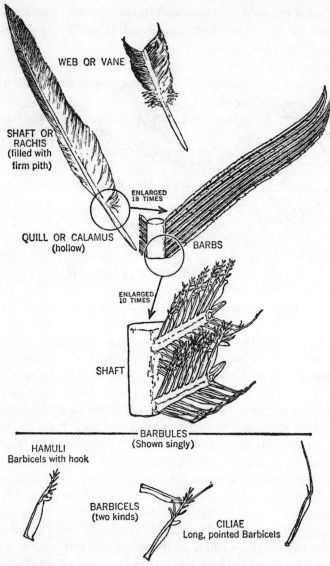

WEB OR VANE

SHAFT OR
RACHIS
(filled with
firm pith)

ENLARGED
18 TIMES

QUILL OR CALAMUS
(hollow)

BARBS

ENLARGED
10 TIMES

SHAFT

BARBULES
(Shown singly)

HAMULI
Barbicels with hook

BARBICELS
(two kinds)

CILIAE
Long, pointed Barbicels

Fig. 10. *The anatomy of a feather. Note how the hamuli hook over the adjacent barbule, locking the web into a firm but flexible structure. If the hooklets become disarranged the bird restores the web by preening.*

that a solid object such as a twig is forced through the feather, the parts of the vane spread apart and permanent damage is avoided. The interlocking barbs and barbules are quickly re-united by preening action of the bird's bill. Bristles are modified contour feathers that appear about the base of the bill and around the eyes of some birds. They are unusually long in fly-catchers and goatsuckers and may aid those birds in catching insects while in flight.

Plumules are the simplest feathers of the adult, and resemble the down of young birds in being loose and soft. They are usu-ally concealed by the contour feathers and provide insulation that retains the bird's body heat and also protects against cold environmental temperature.

Replacement of all feathers of the adult bird normally occurs at least once a year, generally upon completion of the breeding activities. At this time the worn feathers are replaced in a grad-ual and orderly process known as molting. In many birds there is an additional partial or incomplete molt during the year, thus resulting in a plumage that may be composed of feathers of two generations. The feathers of the wings and tail, i.e., those most critical in flight, are generally molted less frequently than the other contour feathers. In most birds only a few of these flight feathers are replaced at one time and the sequence of replacement is such that there is no loss of ability to fly. Excep-tions are to be found among certain water birds, including the ducks, geese, and rails, which shed all their flight feathers si-multaneously and rely on the cover of dense marsh vegetation to hide them from predators for a period of several weeks, while the new feathers grow in. Though most changes in plum-age appearance are achieved by this process of molt, some birds undergo an apparent change in coloration through a wear and loss of feather tips, revealing colors or patterns previously cov-ered. The black throat patch of the House Sparrow is thus fully exposed by late winter as a result of the abrasion of the buffy tips of the black feathers.

Coloration of feathers can be due to pigmentation alone, or to

a combined effect of pigments and feather structure. Three pigments, red, yellow, and brown, account for most of the pigment
coloration of feathers, with the amount of pigment controlling
the intensity of the color and various combinations of the three
pigments producing additional colors. When these pigments are
overlaid with a colorless surface layer, light may be refracted
to produce still different colors. For example, the bright blue
feather of the Blue Jay is actually brown when viewed in the
transmitted light of a microscope. The brown pigment, as normally seen through the refractive surface layer, appears blue to
the human eye (Fig. 11). White feathers have no pigmentation.

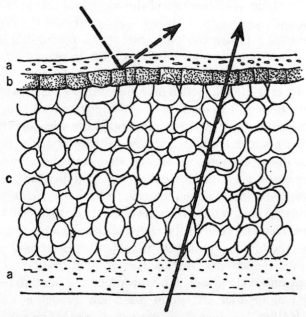

Fig. 11. Section of a length of the barb of a Blue Jay's feather: (a)
sheathing, (b) a layer of blue-producing cells, and (c) pigment cells.
Reflected light would be blue (dotted arrow), but light seen coming
through the feather (solid arrow) would appear brown, from the reaction
of the pigment cells.

In contrast to the highly glandular skin of mammals, a bird's skin is nearly glandless. The only prominent external gland is located at the base of the tail and is called the uropygial gland. Its only secretion has been commonly regarded to be important in the care and waterproofing of the feathers. It is a fact that the gland is usually well developed in aquatic birds, where waterproofing is so essential, and that many birds appear to work the gland when preening their feathers. It would appear that such a function is not an indispensable one, however, for not all birds possess such a gland. Pigeons and parrots have no uropygial gland, for example. Perhaps it serves different purposes in different species. It has been suggested that the oil may be of value in lubricating the horny covering of the bill in some birds, and that for other birds the oil, when irradiated by the sun, may function as a preventative of rickets.

Skeleton and Musculature

In the skeleton we find many examples of specializations and modifications that better adapt birds for their aerial ways. We noted earlier that the bird-like reptiles which gave rise to *Archaeopteryx* were primarily bipedal in their locomotion. Hence their forelimbs, no longer required for walking, were available for modification into organs of flight. There followed a loss of certain bones and a fusion of others to insure maximum rigidity and compactness. Increased porosity and a penetration of bones by air sacs has further lightened the skeleton as a whole. It is important to remember that birds have actually evolved two methods of locomotion, with the forelimbs devoted almost exclusively to flight and the hindlimbs adapted for walking. We shall now see how this division of labor has been achieved with complete harmony between the two stress-resisting systems.

During flight the weight of the bird's body is suspended from the wings, and this is reflected in the much-strengthened shoulder girdle and rib basket. The two clavicles (or "collarbones" of man) are fused to form the familiar "wishbone," which holds the wings away from the breastbone or sternum in the fashion of airplane struts. In most birds the sternum is strengthened by a ventral prominence or keel, which also provides a larger area for the attachment of the powerful pectoral muscles that are responsible for movements of the wing. Consequently the size of the keel is a fair index of wing power. As might be expected, the flightless *Hesperornis* of the Cretaceous period had no keel on its sternum, nor do non-flying birds of the present time, such as the Ostrich, have this structure. Penguins, though flightless, use their wings for swimming and hence possess a keeled sternum. The ribs of birds are fully ossified, unlike those of most mammals, amphibians, and reptiles, and they connect the vertebrae with the sternum to form a rigid thoracic basket. The ribs are further strengthened by uncinate processes which also provide additional sources for attachment of muscles and ligaments (Fig. 12).

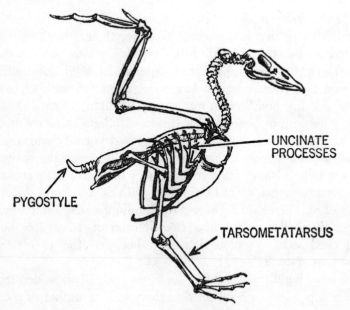

Fig. 12. A bird's skeleton.

The evolution of the wing of birds has been marked by the extensive fusion of some bones and the loss of others, resulting in a remarkably strong yet lightweight structure. The 29 bones to be found in the forelimb of man, for example, have been reduced to 11 in the wing of a pigeon. The first and fifth digits have disappeared, and in most modern birds the hand has lost its claws. There has been, however, a concomitant strengthening of the remaining digits of the hand, for it is this segment of the wing that supports the largest of the flight feathers, the primaries. The second digit (the first as it appears on a bird) is capable of some independent movement and, with the few feathers attached to it, constitutes the alula, an important structure in flight (Fig. 13).

There is relatively little musculature in the wing proper. The movements of the wing are largely controlled by the action of

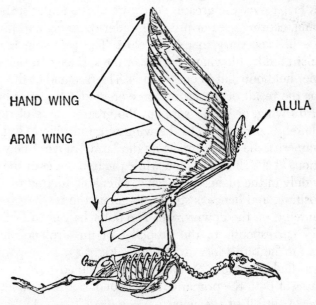

Fig. 13. Wing structure. The flight feathers are attached to the lower arm and to the fused hand. The alula feathers insert on the "thumb" and can be moved separately.

long tendons attached to massive pectoral muscles located on the sternum. Contraction of the outer and larger set of these muscles pulls the wing downward. The inner mass of pectoral muscles, smaller and less powerful, is used to raise the wing. This is accomplished by means of a long tendon that passes over the shoulder, which acts as a pulley, and then attaches to the top of the wing. This illustrates a general feature of avian musculature, namely, the massing of the fleshy and heavier parts of muscles at or toward the center of gravity and provision for their operation by means of unusually long tendons which connect the muscles with the structures that they move. The pectoral muscles alone may represent one-half the total weight of some birds.

A bird's wing serves in a dual capacity, performing the functions of both the wing and the propeller of an airplane. Both an airplane and a bird rely upon the same laws of physics. Air moves faster over the greater curvature of the upper surface of the wing, causing greater pressure under the wing and producing the lift necessary to remain aloft. The principle is easily demonstrated by blowing gently over the surface of a thin piece of paper held outright in one's hands. The free end of the paper rises as the result of the lifting force created. The inner half of the bird's wing, or "arm," supplies the greater share of this lift and thereby corresponds to the wing of an airplane (Fig. 14). The humerus, the bone supporting the "arm," moves freely in all directions at the shoulder joint, while the remainder of the wing bends only in the plane of the wing, to enable folding to a resting position, and hence is stiffened against the resistance of air encountered on the downstroke. The outer half of the wing, or "hand," corresponds to the propeller of an airplane and accounts for the bird's forward motion (Fig. 14). It supports the primary flight feathers. Smaller feathers, called coverts, cover the bases of both the primaries and secondaries to complete the surface or airfoil of the wing.

For many years a popular misconception of the mechanism of bird flight was the belief that as the wing beat down the

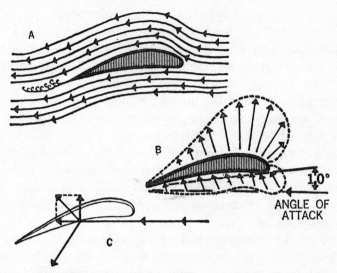

Fig. 14. Flight forces. The speeding up of the air flow on the upper sur-
face produces suction; the slowing down of the air flow across the chord
of the wing produces pressure (a and b). Both result in lift. A second
source of lift at positive angles of attack is the downward deflected por-
tion of the air (c).

bird was lifted up and forward. High-speed photography suggests that the process is not that simple. In normal flight, the
outer half of the wing moves in a semicircle. On the downstroke, the wing tip moves downward and forward, in such a
manner that each of the primaries acts as a small propeller and
assumes the proper pitch to drive the bird forward. The inner
half of the wing moves comparatively little, yet supplies the
necessary lifting force at all times, regardless of the flapping
action of the outer portion. On the upstroke the wing tip
moves upward and backward, pressing against the air and
hence continuing to push the bird along. A figure eight is thus
described by the wing tip in the course of these two components
of flapping flight.

When an airplane reduces its speed, flaps along the trailing
edge of the wing are lowered in order to increase lift and pre-

vent stalling. Birds may accomplish a similar effect by rotating
the entire wing and by depressing and using the tail as a flap.
Stalling may also occur if the angle of the wing increases to a
point where turbulence results in the stream of air passing over
the wing. The apertures or "slots" between the tips of the primaries (Fig. 15) and the use of the alula tend to smooth out
these disturbances and help prevent stalling. These devices for
increasing lift at lowered speeds are especially important upon
landing, where the forward speed must be retarded to insure
against injury. Though some progress has been made in recent
years, with such techniques as high-speed photography and
the use of wind tunnels, we still have much to learn about the
biophysics of bird flight.

Though *Archaeopteryx* had a long, bony tail, there was a reduction of this structure very early in the course of avian evolution. Up to ten of the tail vertebrae have subsequently become
fused into a single bone known as the pygostyle (see Fig. 12),
to which the tail feathers are attached. The remaining tail vertebrae, located in front of the pygostyle, are flexible and permit
movement of the tail feathers in flight maneuvers. Just as the
shoulder girdle had to undergo modifications for support of the
body while in flight, we see that the pelvic girdle has become
fused with the vertebrae of the lower back to provide a rigid,
yet tolerably light structure for the support of the body when
the bird is on the ground. Additional fusion of the bones of the
leg have resulted in a more rigid, yet slenderer hindlimb than
that found in other vertebrates. Some of the tarsal or ankle
bones have become fused with the lower end of the tibia to form
the tibiotarsus, while other tarsal bones have joined with
elongated bones of the foot to form the tarsometatarsus (see
Fig. 12). This results in the fact that birds literally walk on
their toes rather than on their feet. In most birds there are but
four toes. The hallux (or first toe) is pointed backwards and
aids in perching in many species. The bulk of the leg musculature is located on the femur, with long tendons inserting on
the more distal elements.

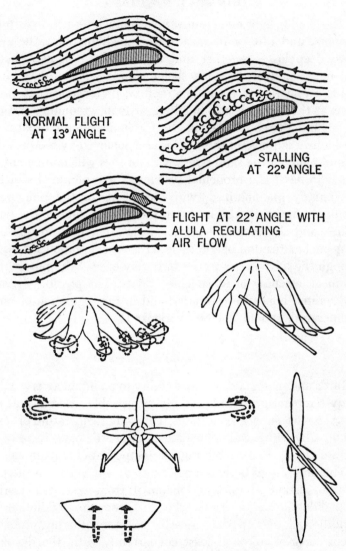

NORMAL FLIGHT
AT 13° ANGLE

STALLING
AT 22° ANGLE

FLIGHT AT 22° ANGLE WITH
ALULA REGULATING
AIR FLOW

*Fig. 15. Efficiency devices. The alula regulates the air flow along the
upper surface of the wing and prevents turbulence at high angles of
attack. The gaps between the primaries serve as wing-tip slots. They mini-
mize induced drag in broad-winged birds and provide forward propul-
sion like the blades of a propeller.*

The skull is light and compact, with much reduction of bony elements and a fusion of most of the remaining ones. The teeth have been lost altogether and replaced by a lighter, horny bill and a relatively light jaw skeleton and musculature. A bird's bill is a remarkably versatile structure, performing such functions as the securing and handling of food, grooming, and defense, and thereby releasing the forelimbs almost exclusively for flight. Lightness of the skull is also achieved by the penetration of many of the skull bones with air sacs which are continuous with nasal and bronchial systems. The postcranial skeleton is similarly pneumatized, with extensions of the pulmonary system of air sacs to be found in the neck vertebrae, the wing bones, and shoulder and pelvic girdles. There is no question that pneumatization of the skeleton is an adaptation for flight, though the advantages to the bird may exceed the purely mechanical lessening of its specific gravity. The possible roles of the aerated bones in respiration and in the regulation of body temperature should not be overlooked.

Homoiothermy

Birds and mammals have the ability to maintain a very stable body temperature in spite of highly variable internal and external environmental conditions. The body temperature of birds is normally within the range of 105° to 111°F., or an increase of from 2° to 14°F. over the normal temperature of mammals.

This stability of body temperature, known as homoiothermy, helps to distinguish birds and mammals from their cold-blooded or poikilothermic ancestors. The shift from the poikilothermic condition of the reptilian ancestry to homoiothermy probably occurred prior to, or at least concurrently with, the development of true flight in birds. The evolution of homoiothermy was effected by a host of structural and physiological modifications in a number of organ systems.

Because of the increased oxygen supply and greater capacity for heat regulation required by their high body temperature, birds have evolved a respiratory system that is perhaps more highly developed than in any other group of animals. This consists of small, relatively inexpansible lungs, and larger, poorly vascularized air sacs. There is a continuous circulation of air through the lungs, via a system of anastomosing (interconnected) passageways. The pulmonary air sacs, usually nine in number, extend these air passages into regions of the neck, breast, and abdomen, and also into the hollow bones of the wing (Fig. 16). There is no muscular diaphragm comparable

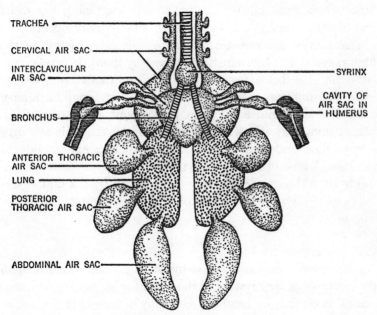

Fig. 16. Respiratory system of a pigeon, showing air sacs and lungs.

to that of mammals, and breathing is accomplished by muscular action of the entire thoracic region, with help from wing movements during flight. These respiratory movements, though working mainly on the air sacs, provide for a continuous passage of air through the lungs. The transfer of oxygen from air to blood and of carbon dioxide from blood to air occurs in the lungs.

Since they lack the sweat glands of mammals, birds rely on other measures to eliminate excess body heat. Panting in birds, for example, is not a sign of exhaustion but rather an effort to speed up dissipation of internal heat by an increased evaporation of moisture from the upper respiratory tract. A resting pigeon normally breathes at a rate of 30–35 per minute. With only a slight increase in body temperature, this rate may exceed 200 per minute (the panting rate). Large amounts of heat are generated during flight which cannot be handled exclusively by panting. It is at such times of heat stress that the air sacs function to great advantage, by greatly increasing the moist surface area over which evaporative cooling may occur.

The highly efficient avian heart is directly related to the high respiratory requirements imposed by flight. It is relatively larger in size, beats faster, and pumps a greater quantity of blood per unit time than the mammalian heart. Small birds have a fantastically rapid basal heart beat, about 400–500 per minute, as compared with a rate of 70–72 in humans. This rate may exceed 1000 under conditions of stress such as extremely cold weather. A flow of fresh, oxygenated blood is maintained separately from the unoxygenated, venous blood by the double circulatory system characteristic of all homoiotherms.

Metabolism

An apparent dilemma posed by the demands of flight upon the avian digestive system is the need for increased fuel consumption on the one hand and economy of weight on the other. Unnecessary overloading of the body is avoided to some extent by a selective diet consisting of a minimum of indigestible material. Then, foodstuffs actually ingested are digested rapidly and efficiently, followed by immediate elimination of wastes.

The function of teeth, which we noted are absent in all living birds, has been replaced in some measure by the biting, grinding, and tearing action of the horny bill. Birds must frequently ingest their food rapidly in order to reduce exposure and vulnerability to predation. This behavior is possible by virtue of a storage capacity of the esophagus. The thin walls of the esophagus are extremely flexible and capable of expanding to hold large items of food which would normally be ground into smaller particles by most other vertebrates. Storage of food may be effected by a temporary dilation of the esophagus or by a more specialized and permanent expansion of this portion of the digestive tract, commonly known as the crop.

There is a unique division of the stomach into a proventriculus or glandular stomach and the ventriculus or muscular stomach (gizzard). The latter, which provides for further mechanical breakdown of foodstuffs, is best developed in granivorous birds, poorly developed in carnivorous and carrion feeders, and absent in fish-eating species. Grit or small stones in the gizzard may be helpful in this grinding process, particularly where seeds and other vegetable matter are involved. Indigestible material, such as bones, fur, and feathers, is regurgitated from the mouth in pellet form without further burden to the system.

Waste products of both the digestive and excretory systems are voided from a common chamber, the cloaca. The large intestine of birds is relatively short and residual wastes from digestive processes are eliminated rapidly. There is no bladder, thus eliminating the weight of stored urine. The latter, high in uric acid content, is carried directly from the kidneys to the cloaca where it is voided in a semisolid state.

Sensory Capacities

Among the various organ systems of birds, not the least influenced by the demands of flight has been the nervous system. This influence has been exercised directly in the case of a need for coordinating and positioning the body in flight, and indirectly with regard to sensory perception in behavior patterns that have been modified by flight. Notable differences in the bird brain (Fig. 17), upon comparison with that of other vertebrates, are the very prominent centers of integration of motor

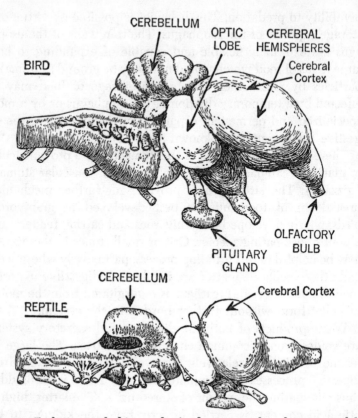

CEREBELLUM

OPTIC LOBE

CEREBRAL HEMISPHERES
Cerebral Cortex

BIRD

OLFACTORY BULB

PITUITARY GLAND

CEREBELLUM

Cerebral Cortex

REPTILE

Fig. 17. Early in reptile history the forebrain was altered in two widely divergent directions. In one, leading up to the birds, the side walls of the forebrain were greatly thickened by the further development of the corpus striatum, that part of the brain concerned with stereotyped, relatively unmodifiable behavior. In the other, leading to the mammals, the side walls thickened much less and the upper part of the forebrain, the cerebral cortex, increased in size and complexity. In man, this portion of the brain which is concerned with memory, conscious behavior, and the ability to learn, constitutes the main part of the brain mass. In addition to the complex corpus striatum in the forebrain, birds also have two greatly enlarged optic lobes. The hearing center in the hindbrain is well developed; the olfactory or smell area of the brain is small.

activities such as the cerebral hemispheres and cerebellum. Well-developed semi-circular canals and associated structures within the inner ear help to provide for equilibrium in flight.

The optic lobes of the bird's brain are relatively larger than those of other vertebrates, including man, attesting to the degree to which birds are dependent upon vision. The eyes are disproportionately large and not spherically shaped as in man (Fig. 18). The unique shape of the eyeball results in a considerable economy of space and weight with no corresponding loss of optical efficiency. The retina of the avian eye is not profusely supplied with blood vessels, as is the case in the human eye. Nutrients, supplied by the pecten, presumably reach the retinal cells by diffusion through the vitreous humor.

The visual acuity of most birds is no better than that of man. Birds of prey that depend upon discrimination of food from considerable distances probably exceed man in this capacity, but it has been demonstrated that some of the smaller song birds have an acuity that is actually inferior to that of man. Where birds do excel is in the rate at which they are able to assimilate detail within the visual field. They are capable of registering, with but a brief glance, a complete scene which the human eye can appreciate only by a piecemeal scanning of the whole field. Birds apparently perceive colors with much the same precision as do humans.

This rapid assimilation and high degree of resolution throughout the visual field, characteristic of the avian eye, offers a possible explanation for the navigational abilities that have been attributed to birds in a number of recent studies of how birds migrate (see Chapter 4). Inherent in one of the prominent theories proposed is an ability to accurately estimate the rate of change of the elevation and azimuth of the sun, a feat well beyond the capabilities of the unaided human eye.

The eyes of most birds are located on the sides of the head and are only slightly movable in their sockets. The Robin that cocks its head when hunting for food is not listening, as commonly believed, but instead is bringing its eye into a position for

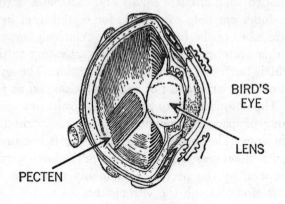

BIRD'S
EYE

LENS

PECTEN

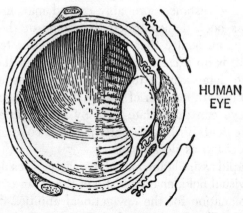

HUMAN
EYE

Fig. 18. The rear wall of the avian eye is flattened so that most of the visual field is always "in focus." Focusing is done by bulging or flattening the very elastic lens. The number of visual elements per unit area of the retina is three times as great in some birds as in man. Most of them are cells specialized for color vision. Vision is further improved by especially sensitive areas on the retina.

better vision. This immobility of the eyes reaches an extreme in owls and is compensated for by having greater flexibility of the neck, permitting rotation of the head through an arc of nearly 270 degrees.

It may come as a surprise to some readers to know that birds have ears, for the entrance to the ear is normally obscured by a covering of feathers. The absence of pinnae, the outer ears so conspicuous in most mammals, is correlated with the need to reduce air friction. It should be noted, however, that bats have apparently circumvented this disadvantage to the extent of even increasing the relative size of these appendages. It would seem that in the absence of pinnae there may be some loss of absolute and directional sensitivity, but the covering of feathers over the ear opening probably serves to reduce turbulence and the masking effect of undesirable noise.

Most birds are unable to hear frequencies as high as those within the audible range of mammals. But within the frequency range to which they are sensitive, birds appear to have a better sense of time discrimination. In fact, studies suggest that the principal auditory receptor, the cochlea, has a speed of response that is about ten times more rapid in birds than in humans. This means that, though the ears are closer together in birds and consequently the time interval to be discriminated is less, the directional sensitivity is probably equal to or better than that of man. Birds also appear to be better able to differentiate between various intensities of sound.

The primary role played by the ear, in so far as flight is concerned, is not in hearing but in the maintenance of equilibrium. A portion of the inner ear consists of a closed system of liquid-filled sacs and semicircular canals, one for each plane in space. Movement of the liquid in these structures is registered by sensory hairs, thereby relaying information to the cerebellum of the brain as to the movement of the bird and the position of its body in space. The cerebellum, a nerve center for the reflexive coordination and control of movement and equilibrium, is exceptionally large and well developed in birds.

3 VARIATIONS ON A GENERAL THEME

The great diversity of the kinds of birds found throughout the world is at once impressive and provocative. These are the living products of a long historical process of evolution; still other kinds have appeared at various levels during geological time only to disappear at some later stage. Working with fundamentals established by Charles Darwin a century ago, biologists have arrived at a reasonable interpretation of the evolutionary processes involved. Genetic variability, adaptation, environmental change, survival, and extinction—these are the ingredients of the recipe that has produced this remarkable pageantry of avian diversity down through the ages.

The Nature of Adaptations

Geneticists tell us that the gene is the fundamental unit of inheritance by which the potential for characteristics is passed from one generation to the next. Any organism is the product of the interaction of thousands of these genes with each other and with the immediate environment. The total complement of genes in a single organism constitutes a genotype. In each succeeding generation genes are recombined from the vast pool of genes within the population at large, resulting in an infinite variety of genotypes or organisms with differing potentialities of development. Not all of these genotypes are equally well equipped to survive in their particular environment. Those that are superior or are able to adjust to environmental change have a greater probability of surviving to reproductive age and of leaving a greater number of offspring. Any genetic variation that helps the organism to survive and succeed in its environment can be called an adaptation. All adaptations, and hence the very trend of evolution itself, are controlled through a molding effect of the environment which is commonly referred to as natural selection.

Birds are particularly suitable as subjects for a study of adaptations. On the one hand they are unusually uniform in their basic structure. This structural uniformity is in itself due to a number of generalized adaptations, pursued in the previous chapter, which have prepared birds for flight. But in addition to these, most birds exhibit specialized types of adaptations which enable particular birds to occupy their particular niches or modes of life. These special adaptations of the basic pattern of avian anatomy and physiology are responsible for the great diversity of the kinds of birds that we see around us. In this chapter we will consider some of the more outstanding examples of these adaptations and the selective forces that have determined their evolution. We will also consider the need for organizing the entities of this diversification into a meaningful system of classification.

Body Size

Variations in the size of birds are related to a balance between such factors as the amount of food ingested, heat loss from the body, and the demands of flight. Since smaller birds lose more heat relative to their body size than do larger birds, there is a minimum size below which birds are incapable of ingesting and metabolizing sufficient amounts of food to offset this heat loss. Some of the hummingbirds apparently circumvent this limitation upon smallness by lowering their body temperature during periods of inactivity or when food is difficult to obtain. The smallest of all birds, the Bee Hummingbird of Cuba, measures slightly over two inches from tip of bill to tip of tail and weighs less than two grams.

The maximum size attainable by flying birds is basically a function of wing loading and the speed of flight. By wing loading we mean the weight of the body relative to the area of the wing available for support. If two birds have the same body form and wing shape, but differ in size and weight, the larger bird must fly faster than the smaller one in order to remain aloft. By decreasing their effective wing load through variations in wing shape many birds have been able to modify this maximum permissible size. Birds that soar, or take advantage of thermal air currents that are often deflected upward along mountain ridges or shore lines, have comparatively light wing loads. While the tiny chickadee, which weighs less than half an ounce, may have a wing load of as much as 0.3 pounds per square foot, the five-pound vulture may have a wing load of only 1.1 pound per square foot. The chickadee, with so small a wing area in relation to body weight, must flap its wings more rapidly. In general, the smaller the wing in relation to body weight, the faster it must beat to provide sufficient lift. Many soaring birds have wings that are long in relation to their width—engineers say that they have a high "aspect ratio." The Wandering Albatross has an extremely high aspect ratio and its eleven-foot wing span is among the largest of all living birds. In some large birds, such as the pelican, the bones are highly pneumatic and there are extensions of the air sacs beneath the skin. The Great Bustard of Eurasia may be the heaviest of all flying birds, for there are records of males weighing as much as 37 pounds.

Locomotion

The ability to fly has been lost in the Ostrich, the largest of living birds, which stands eight feet tall and weighs over 300 pounds. There is no suggestion of a keel on its sternum, but there has been a compensatory development of the hindlimb to enable it to carry its weight at a running gait. A similar loss of the keeled breastbone has occurred in the flightless descendants of several old evolutionary lines, including the rheas, emus, and extinct moas and elephant birds. Flightlessness has apparently developed quite secondarily among a number of unrelated groups of birds, for there are flightless representatives among the following groups, most of whose members are capale of flight: grebes, ducks, rails, cormorants, and parrots. None of the flightless members of these groups has completely lost the keel on the sternum, though it is poorly developed in all of them.

Another group of flightless birds, the penguins, has developed compensatory adaptations for swimming and are among the most truly marine of all birds. Their forelimbs have no flight feathers and have evolved into short, powerful flippers which they use literally to "fly" through the water. The keel has been retained on the sternum, reflecting the massive muscle power used in operating the flippers.

A group of birds of northern seas, collectively known as alcids and including such familiar forms as the puffins and murres, have modified the basic avian design to permit both aerial flight and underwater "flying." Their wings represent a compromise adaptation between large wings required for flight and small wings that can be effectively used as paddles under water. The largest member of this group, the Great Auk, became flightless as a result of an unfavorable compromise between large body size and small wing. Its helplessness on land led to its extermination by man in the early 1800's. The difficulty which flightless birds have in escaping predators has, as a rule, resulted in their restriction to limited areas where there are few enemies or the adaptation of some compensatory method of escape such as running or hiding.

Adaptations among birds for locomotion in and beneath the water are most striking in the hindlimbs. Diving birds that are largely foot-propelled, such as the loons and grebes, have extremely well-developed musculature of the hindlimbs. The feet are located far back on the body and operated with great mobility above, below, or on a level with the body when under water. Their "legs" (tarsometatarsi) are conspicuously flattened to reduce water drag. An associated adaptation for diving includes a reduction in buoyancy through loss of pneumaticity of the skeleton and an ability to rapidly expel air from the air sacs and from the plumage.

Swimming birds generally have feet that are either webbed or lobed to serve as paddles. The usual condition is for the webbing to involve only three toes, the rear toe remaining free, as among the ducks, gulls, and penguins. Pelicans have the rear toe included within the webbing. Grebes have extensions of the skin or lobes along each side of the toe which flatten out against the water on the power stroke and fold inward to reduce water drag on the recovery (Fig. 19).

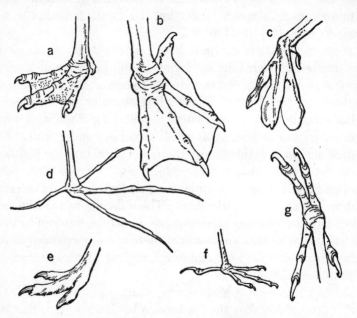

Fig. 19. Adaptations of the feet of birds: (a) *duck,* (b) *pelican,* (c) *grebe,* (d) *jacana,* (e) *ptarmigan,* (f) *pipit,* (g) *woodpecker.*

Long-legged, short-toed birds that do a great deal of running, like the Secretary Bird of Africa, have had to cope with the problem of balance and stability. In order to retain the center of gravity over the feet, especially when it crouches or settles to the ground, the tibiotarsus and tarsometatarsus have remained approximately the same length. Long-legged wading birds such as the herons and flamingos have solved this problem in a similar fashion.

Lengthened toes and claws appear in a variety of birds as a means of walking on mud or other unstable substrate. The jacana exhibits the extreme in length of toes and claws, an adaptation for walking on the floating vegetation of tropical ponds. Among the smaller land birds there are groups such as the larks and pipits which spend much of their time running on soft ground, and they have developed elongated claws for better traction. Broad, densely feathered toes help to support the Asian Sand Grouse on sand and true grouse such as the ptarmigan on snow.

Many of the smaller land birds have a remarkable arrangement of the tendons of the foot, which is an adaptation for perching. The tendons of those muscles that normally extend the toes pass behind the ankle joint. When the ankle joint is flexed, as in a perching position, tension is applied to these tendons and the toes are automatically locked in a firm grasp of the branch.

Birds that habitually climb on tree trunks or rock surfaces generally have a much shortened hindlimb and strongly curved claws. Some, like the woodpeckers and tree creepers, also use their tails as support, in which case the pygostyle is considerably enlarged and the tail feathers modified for greater strength.

Feeding

The influence of the environment upon the basic pattern of avian anatomy is particularly evident in the diverse adaptations for obtaining and handling food. These primarily involve modifications of the bill and tongue (Fig. 20), and to a lesser extent the feet.

Birds that feed upon insects and other small invertebrates frequently rely upon a short, thin bill which they manipulate like forceps in picking food from the vegetation. The slightly decurved bills of the tree creepers also permit probing into the

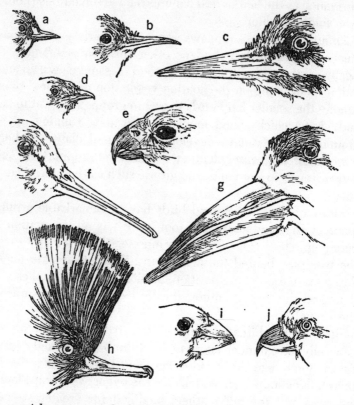

Fig. 20. Adaptations of the bills of birds: (*a*) *warbler*, (*b*) *creeper*, (*c*) *woodpecker*, (*d*) *swallow*, (*e*) *hawk*, (*f*) *woodcock*, (*g*) *skimmer*, (*h*) *merganser*, (*i*) *grosbeak*, (*j*) *crossbill*.

crevices of bark. Woodpeckers have evolved a stronger, chisel-shaped bill with which they can actually remove pieces of bark and decaying wood in their search for wood-boring insects. The broad, flat bills of swallows and flycatchers enlarge the effective area of the mouth so that insects can also be scooped up while in flight. Ground-dwelling invertebrates are at the mercy of the woodcock, which has a long, narrow bill for probing in the soft earth. Aquatic invertebrates are removed from pond water by

he straining action of a series of laminations along the edges
of the bills of ducks and geese.

Fish-eating birds often have serrations or hook-like structures
along each edge of the bill that provide a firmer grasp of their
ood. The long, sharp bills of herons and kingfishers are effective
either as spears or as forceps in obtaining fish. A unique adap-
ation for scooping up fish appears in the skimmers: the lower
mandible, noticeably longer than the upper one, is submerged
and operated like a plow while the birds skim over the surface
of the water. When the bill strikes a fish, the upper bill closes
ightly on the slippery prey and the meal is promptly swallowed
n flight. The bills of hawks and owls and other carnivorous
birds are typically strong and hooked, for tearing flesh into
pieces small enough to swallow.

Short, stout bills generally suggest a seed or granivorous diet.
An extreme development in this direction is exhibited by the
Hawfinch, capable of exerting a force of nearly 100 pounds with
its massive, crushing bill. Crossbills have the tips of the man-
dibles overlapping in a unique specialization for removing seeds
from the cones of trees.

The tongue of seed- and insect-eating birds is typically a
thin structure, slightly bushy at the tip, and armed with back-
ward-projecting spines along the sides. In hummingbirds and
honeycreepers that feed largely on pollen and nectar, the
tongue is exceptionally long and its sides are rolled inward,
facilitating the extraction of this food from deep within flowers.
In some species the tongue is actually tubular and is used as
a straw to suck up the nectar. Woodpeckers have unusually
ong, slender, and barbed tongues used in the manner of a har-
poon to extract wood-boring insects.

The claws of hawks and owls are modified into long and
powerful talons for grasping and holding prey. An Asiatic owl
that feeds primarily on fish has spiny scales on the soles of its
feet that enable it to hold its slippery food. Many ground-feed-
ng birds have well-developed legs and feet that are specialized
for scratching within the ground litter.

Physiology

Among the numerous physiological adaptations that better equip birds for survival in their respective environments is one involving metabolism in the Lesser Honey-guide of Africa. This remarkable bird is capable of living for extended periods of time upon nothing but bees' wax, a substance long considered by scientists as indigestible, at least by higher animals. Recent studies suggest that microbes living within the bird's digestive tract are responsible for metabolizing the wax and thus making nutrients available to their host. When denied this assistance from its intestinal fauna, the Lesser Honey-guide is unable to digest and utilize the wax.

Another remarkable adaptation accounts for the ability of sea birds to survive without fresh water to drink. In mammals and most birds the kidney is the principal organ responsible for the removal of excess salts from the blood. But the avian kidney is capable of excreting salts in a concentration only about one-half that found in sea water. Marine birds, including some gulls, pelicans, and cormorants, have extremely well-developed glands located at the base of the bill, just above the eyes. These nasal glands are thought to be the principal organ for excretion of salt, since they are capable of producing fluids with salt concentrations higher than that in ingested sea water. This adaptation of birds to their environment has been shown experimentally, for when marine birds of the same species are raised in salt water and in fresh water, those exposed to salt water have considerably larger nasal glands.

We noted in the chapter on general, systemic adaptations for flight that birds normally maintain a very stable and comparatively high body temperature, concomitant with an over-all speed-up of metabolic activity. But a few birds have found it advantageous to modify this homoiothermy. Hummingbirds, for example, have a higher metabolic rate than that known for any other animal. Some species are able to conserve much of this energy by reducing their body temperature and metabolic activity each night. In this torpid state, their temperature may drop as much as 30°F. and breathing may cease completely for several minutes' duration. Torpidity can also be advantageous to birds whose food consists principally of flying insects. When these insects are scarce, as during periods of inclement weather, certain species of swifts and goatsuckers are known to become torpid and thus ride out the period of fasting.

One species of goatsucker, the Poor-will of western North America, has succeeded in extending the torpid period from one of several hours in length to as long as several months. Recent findings prove that at least some Poor-wills enter rock crevices at the onset of winter, when flying insects become scarce, rather than migrate southward with the majority of insectivorous birds. There they remain, with greatly reduced metabolic activity and a body temperature some 30°–40°F. below normal, until the first warming trend of spring. Such an extended period of torpidity resembles hibernation as practiced by certain mammals and most poikilothermic animals of northern latitudes.

Other physiological adaptations that merit attention here have to do with the remarkable sensory abilities that have been developed by birds whose activities are often performed in total darkness. Though it is true that the vision of owls is superior to that of most animals under conditions of poor illumination, owls are helpless in total darkness, contrary to popular opinion. The survival value of any other sensory mechanism by which owls can locate their prey in the absence of light is at once apparent. Barn Owls are able to locate mice in total darkness solely on the basis of the sounds that the mice make by their movements in the ground litter. The intensity of these sounds, as heard by the owl, varies with the angle from which the sound is received. The owl's ability to accurately orient toward the sound is apparently augmented by the unique, asymmetrical position of the ears, with one ear opening being above and the other below the horizontal plane. The owl turns its head in an attempt to match the intensity of the sound in both ears, thereby facing the sound directly.

The Oilbird, which nests and roosts in caves of northern South America, has solved this problem of activity in total darkness in a different manner. When light is available, the Oilbird orients by means of the usual visual cues, for its eyes are roughly as large as those of other birds of comparable size. But in the darker recesses of its cave, it emits clicking sounds and is able to detect and avoid obstacles in its flight path by virtue of the echoes created by these sounds. This system of echolocation utilizes sounds that are audible to the human ear, much as a blind person uses his cane, and unlike the supersonic emissions that serve a similar purpose for bats. Certain species of swifts that live in caves in southern Asia have adopted a means of echolocation similar to that of the Oilbird.

Plumage Coloration

The patterns and colors of bird plumages contribute in large measure to the diversification that we see in the bird world, and in many instances it is not difficult to judge the adaptive significance of these plumage differences. Two functions most frequently attributed to a bird's coloration are concealment and display. It would appear that natural selective pressures toward one or the other of these contradictory functions have varied greatly among species, though a few species may have successfully evolved compromising plumages to serve both objectives.

Most birds are in constant danger of attack from predators. Their ability to fly is, of course, an important survival mechanism affording escape from terrestrial enemies, but the best deterrent to sudden attack from the air would appear to be a concealing or cryptic coloration. Effective camouflage has been achieved through several different principles, including simulation or mimicry of a characteristic background and a reduction of the visible solidity of the bird by breaking up its apparent outline.

In most birds the light and dark colors of the plumage are arranged in a manner that counteracts the effect of self-shadowing. The darker colors are usually on the upper parts, where the light is stronger, and the paler colors are below and often in shadow. This distribution of the plumage colors to counterbalance the unequal lighting received by the various parts of the body is known as countershading (Fig. 21).

Fig. 21. *Countershading and color resemblance in the Sanderling; color resemblance without countershading in the White-tailed Ptarmigan where the bird's visual solidity and its shadow make it more noticeable.* (*After Plate 3 of Friedman,* War Background Studies, *No. 5, 1942.*)

The prevalence of greenish birds in the forest canopy and predominantly brownish birds on the forest floor and in other ground niches exemplifies the general trend toward a resemblance of plumage coloration to the bird's immediate surroundings. For similar reasons, presumably, shore birds like the Sanderling (see Fig. 46) have evolved a "salt and pepper mottling" that blends them with their background. This matching of plumage with habitat may vary geographically between different populations of a single species, as in the Song Sparrow of North America, where individuals that live in desert regions are extremely pale and those that live in humid areas are darker (Fig. 22). Furthermore, the seasonal changes in plumage coloration of the ptarmigan, from white in winter to brown in summer, are adaptively in tune with seasonal changes in the prevailing colors of its northern environment.

Fig. 22. There are 33 recognized races of Song Sparrows, each occupying a different habitat in North America. Shown here are (a) a dark-plumaged race adapted to the humid northwest coast; (b) a light-plumaged race adapted to its dry habitat in the southwestern desert; and (c) a race of intermediate coloration found throughout eastern North America.

Still other birds, like the Ring-necked Plover, achieve concealment by means of disruptive coloration. Plumage patterns with irregular, sharply defined areas of contrasting colors tend to break up the general contour of the bird and are more conspicuous, when seen at a distance, than the bird itself (Fig. 23).

Fig. 23. The effect of disruptive coloring in the Ring-necked Plover. At the left, the bird is against its normal background; at the right, without the background. (After Plate 9 of Friedman, War Background Studies, No. 5, 1942.)

Far from being cryptically marked, a great many birds are at once conspicuous because of brilliant colors or elaborate plumes or other feather modifications. The chief function and selective value of these conspicuous plumages is thought to be the bringing together of the sexes during the breeding season. The males of most species are more brilliantly colored than the females and they frequently feature ornamental feathers which are displayed prominently during the courtship period. The conspicuousness of the male makes him more often the object of pursuit by predators, while the duller-colored female incubates and protects her brood. The reversal of this arrangement of a more brightly colored male is found among a very few species, including phalaropes, in which the male is the duller plumaged. In these birds, significantly, it is the female that courts the male and the male that incubates the eggs.

In those birds in which the choice of a breeding partner is largely a visual process, it is clear how this sexual dimorphism might have evolved. In the competition for mates, males having the more conspicuous colors or markings would have an ad-

Fig. 24. *Individual variability of the Ruff. In contrast to the simply colored female (in the center) the male may have a black, brown, white, grayish, plain, or barred ruff, and may vary in other parts of the body from individual to individual.*

vantage. This reproductive advantage, known as sexual selection, would thus tend to increase the degree of difference between the sexes of a species. Sexual selection probably is most intense in species like the Ruff, in which several males perform on a common display ground or lek, to which the females come and make their choice for fertilization (Fig. 24).

Classification of Birds

The great diversity of the kinds of birds has been a challenge to the human mind. Laymen and scientists alike abhor disorder and appreciate the necessity for naming and classifying living organisms. Early attempts at the classification of birds consisted of little more than pragmatic systems of "pigeonholes," much as a child might put a collection of building blocks in order according to their size, shape, and color. The emphasis in such a classification is on morphological differences. Blocks are placed in separate piles whenever they appear different to the eye. Similarly, there was a time when the male and female Mallard were classified as two separate species because they were morphologically distinct. Biologists now recognize the fallacy of such a limited criterion and make a deliberate effort to see to it that the categories of classification are made to coincide as closely as possible with the natural affinities of the animals that they include, based on a common descent of these organisms. Our current classification of birds is based on a synthesis of information from many fields of biology, including comparative anatomy and morphology, paleontology, ecology, physiology, behavior, zoogeography, and protein chemistry.

The Biological Species

The objective basis for this modern classification is the concept of the biological species, in which great emphasis is placed upon the potential for interbreeding between different populations. Since reproductive criteria are frequently unavailable, it is fortunate indeed that the reproductive gaps maintained between species are accompanied in most cases by morphological gaps as well. Some examples using familiar birds will serve to illustrate the basic principles that are followed in taxonomy, the practice of recognizing and formalizing the relationships among living organisms.

The Redwinged Blackbird is a well-known bird throughout much of North and Middle America. Redwings breed only with other Redwings. We know this on the basis of field observations and we can also infer it from the fact that no morphological hybrids, which would have resulted from the interbreeding of Redwings and other kinds of birds, have ever been found. This fulfills the requirement of the biological species concept and we refer to the Redwing as a species.

Though the name "Redwing" may be adequate in communications within the United States, it carries an entirely different connotation for English-speaking Europeans, who apply the same name to one of their common thrushes (Fig. 25). Fur-

Fig. 25. A source of confusion in common names: the Redwinged Blackbird (left) and the European Redwing. (After Peterson.)

thermore, the species known as the "Redwing" in the United States is called the *Tordo charretero* in Mexico. To circumvent these inadequacies of common or vernacular names, biologists have agreed on an internationally accepted code of nomenclature or system of names whereby each species receives a combination of two names. Thus, the scientific name of the Redwing (of North America) is *Agelaius phoeniceus,* which is applicable to all populations of the species.

Because their preferred habitat has a discontinuous type of distribution, individuals of *Agelaius phoeniceus* are not distributed in a continuous or uniform fashion throughout the range of the species. These discontinuous populations, though potentially capable of interbreeding, exhibit varying degrees of morphological differentiation. The birds within the Central Valley of California, for example, generally have solid red shoulders which lack the buffy edgings so characteristic of other populations. To better understand geographical variation within the species as a whole, biologists consider it advantageous to acknowledge and name this divergent population, and this is accomplished according to the international code by adding a third or modifying name. Thus the central Californian population of Redwings becomes *Agelaius phoeniceus californicus,* which identifies it as a *subspecies* of *Agelaius phoeniceus.* The concept of the subspecies does not have the reality of the species category, for the decision as to how much divergence in a population is necessary to warrant its subspecific recognition is largely a subjective matter. Some 24 subspecies of *Agelaius phoeniceus* are currently recognized.

In the marshes of California there is another bird called the Tricolored Blackbird, which so closely resembles the Redwing that it is seldom differentiated by the casual observer. However, it does differ from the more widespread form with respect to several morphological features (taxonomic characters), and the distinction is not difficult to make once these are known. The significant point here is that both of these closely related blackbirds frequently are to be found breeding within the same marsh and without evidence of interbreeding or intergradation of morphological characters. This fact establishes specific status for the Tricolored Blackbird, and it has been named *Agelaius tricolor. Agelaius* is the generic portion of this name and serves a function similar to our surname. It refers exclusively to a group of blackbirds—no other animals bear this generic term in their scientific names. The generic term, or *genus,* serves as a category to which are assigned all of the specific names of very closely related species, including *tricolor* and *phoeniceus* in this instance.

In cases where two populations are separated geographically, the decision as to whether they are separate species or but geographical variants or subspecies cannot, of course, be based on reproductive isolation, or a lack thereof. Here we must rely upon comparative observations of the morphology and total biology of the two forms, and weigh these with respect to variation among other forms within the genus. Thus *Agelaius thilius,* the Yellow-shouldered Marsh Bird of western and southern South America, has no opportunity to interbreed with *Agelaius phoeniceus* or *Agelaius tricolor,* yet radical color differences in its plumage suggest that it would not do so if given that opportunity.

Most if not all species of birds have probably arisen as the result of having been separated geographically from similar populations long enough to have permitted the development of crucial genetic differences. The degree of genetic divergence may be tested at a later time, should the incipient species extend its range to overlap that of the parental form. If the isolating mechanisms are adequate, the two forms will maintain their reproductive integrity. Each of these newly created species is an experiment in adaptation, in that it differs from other species in its relationship with the environment. We have already noted that some of them represent failures in adaptation and will not survive.

How many species of birds are there? Because of lack of information about the probability of interbreeding among many populations, we must be content with an educated guess which places the number at about 8600. By way of comparison, there are almost more species of birds than there are species of mammals (3500) and reptiles and amphibians (5500) combined.

But there are probably well over one million species of animals, with two groups accounting for about 84 per cent of this total: insects (750,000) and mollusks (88,000). Probably less than half of the insects of the world have been named. Birds, however, are known better than any other major group of animals and it is doubtful that as many as 100 species remain to be discovered.

Higher Taxonomic Categories

We have seen that closely related species of birds are grouped together into units known as genera. In addition to having a common origin, the species occupying any one genus are generally adapted for a particular way of life; e.g., the species of *Agelaius* are typically colonial—nesting blackbirds of marshes and open fields. Genera of common ancestry are in turn arranged into still higher units of the taxonomic hierarchy known as families. Thus we find that *Agelaius* is grouped with other genera of blackbirds such as *Molothrus* (cowbirds), *Quiscalus* (grackles), and *Icterus* (orioles) to form the family Icteridae. The Icteridae are assigned to one of the approximately 28 major orders of living birds, the Passeriformes, which includes all of the so-called song birds of the world.

In the taxonomic hierarchy, then, each group is composed of those units of the next lower level which share a number of biological and structural characters that distinguish them from members of other groups at the same level. The exact limits of these taxonomic groups are left to the subjective judgment of the taxonomists, the scientists who specialize in the classification of animals.

Recent attempts to arrange the higher taxonomic categories of birds in a meaningful sequence have been aimed at reconstructing their evolutionary history (Fig. 26). Since birds have evolved much as a tree grows, in a many-branched three-dimensional pattern, a classification expressed in a linear sequence will have obvious limitations. In addition, there are problems of

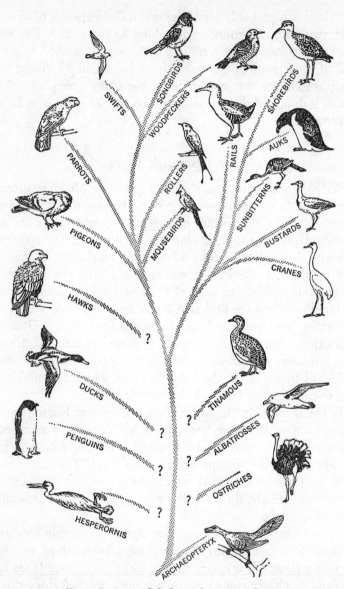

SWIFTS

SONGBIRDS

WOODPECKERS

SHOREBIRDS

PARROTS

RAILS

AUKS

ROLLERS

SUNBITTERNS

PIGEONS

MOUSEBIRDS

BUSTARDS

CRANES

HAWKS

?

DUCKS

TINAMOUS

?

PENGUINS

ALBATROSSES

?

?

OSTRICHES

?

HESPERORNIS

?

ARCHAEOPTERYX

Fig. 26. *A simplified family tree of birds.*

interpretation involved. Though the over-all trend of the evolution of animals has been from the simple to the complex, this concept is of little value in interpreting the pattern of evolution within a particular group such as birds. The fact that the song birds of the order Passeriformes are placed at the "higher" end of our classification and the waterfowl (order Anseriformes) at the "lower" end is not because song birds are considered to be more *complex* than are ducks and geese. Furthermore, the positioning of certain birds at the beginning of a linear sequence does not necessarily imply that these particular birds are nearer the ancestral-type bird than are other living birds. In most instances it does suggest that these "lower" birds are the living representatives of groups which have an older evolutionary origin than many of the "higher" groups. Their position at the lower end of the classification suggests in many instances a high degree of specialization and hence little potential for adaptive evolution. By contrast, birds placed at the upper end of the sequence, including the Icteridae and other families of the Passeriformes, are believed to be exhibiting a rapid and extensive adaptive radiation.

Adaptive Radiation and Convergence

An outstanding illustration of this process of adaptive radiation among the more recently evolved groups is to be found in the Drepanididae, a family of small- to medium-sized song birds that live on the Hawaiian Islands and are known collectively as the Hawaiian Honeycreepers (Fig. 27). Early investigators were so impressed with the great diversity in bill and tongue structure and feeding habits of these birds that they classified them as representatives of several avian families. The inclination was understandable, for within this array of insular populations one finds: bills slightly twisted at the tip like those of crossbills and used for securing insects beneath the scales of leaf buds; long, decurved bills for probing crevices for insects; strong bills used to hammer on bark in woodpecker fashion;

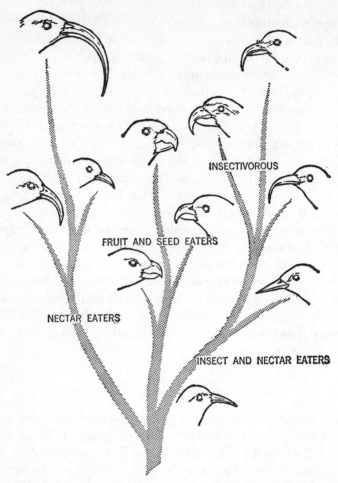

INSECTIVOROUS

FRUIT AND SEED EATERS

NECTAR EATERS

INSECT AND NECTAR EATERS

Fig. 27. *Each species of bird is adapted for some particular mode of life or ecological niche. When the ancestor of the various species of Hawaiian Honeycreeper arrived in the Hawaiian Islands, it found a rich and diversified tropical habitat, but almost no competition from other birds. This stimulated the invasion of one ecological niche after another, leading to a unique degree of adaptive radiation. The family tree shows how species, highly modified for securing such foods as nectar, bark insects, and seeds, have evolved from a simpler ancestral species by changes in feeding habits.*

heavy, stout bills for crushing large seeds; and narrow, pointed bills used in probing flowers for nectar. Upon re-examination, it now appears certain that all of these diverse forms originated from a common ancestral emigrant from the North American mainland, whose exact identity is still subject to speculation. The divergence among the various members of the family has occurred relatively recently, for the Hawaiian Islands are young geologically. That the radiation was so rapid and extensive is probably related to the absence of other competing groups on

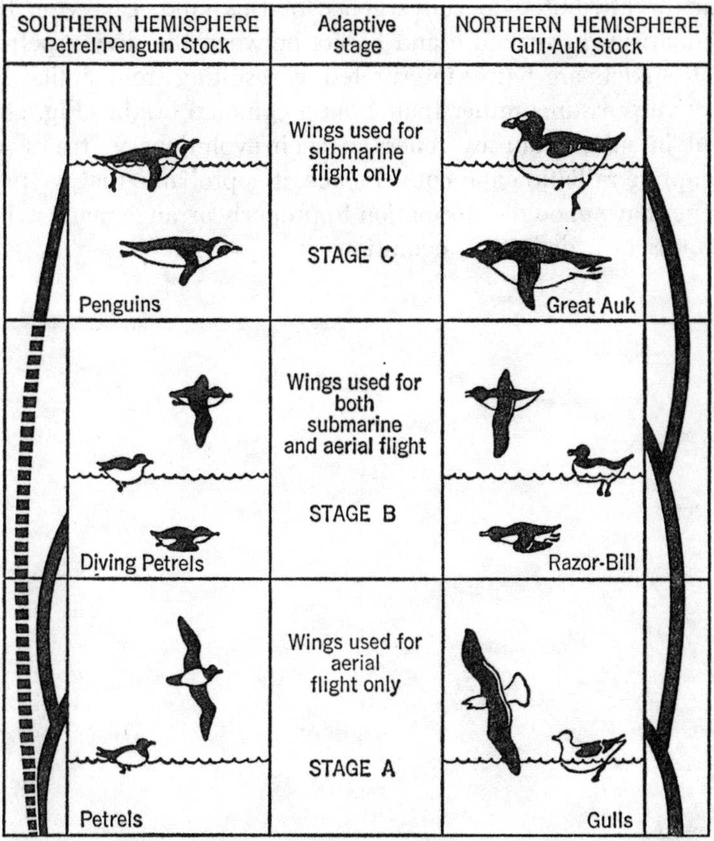

SOUTHERN HEMISPHERE Petrel-Penguin Stock	Adaptive stage	NORTHERN HEMISPHERE Gull-Auk Stock
Penguins	Wings used for submarine flight only STAGE C	Great Auk
Diving Petrels	Wings used for both submarine and aerial flight STAGE B	Razor-Bill
Petrels	Wings used for aerial flight only STAGE A	Gulls

Fig. 28. Convergent evolution in two stocks of diving birds. (After Storer.)

these oceanic islands, the great variety of unexploited environmental niches, and the impetus to the rate of speciation provided by the various geographically isolated island populations

One of the major problems in this attempt to arrive at a classification of birds consistent with their evolution is the real possibility that superficially similar birds may develop in very
different and unrelated groups by virtue of their adaptation to
similar ecological niches. We have already noted that recent
studies suggest that the common characters shared by the large
flightless birds, including the Ostrich, rhea, and elephant bird
can be attributed to convergence of this kind. Likewise, the
similarities in structure and habits between the diving petrel
and auklets are better interpreted as resulting from similar selective pressures rather than from a common origin (Fig. 28)
But in spite of an awareness of such evolutionary "tricks" a
adaptive radiation and convergence, it is probable that we may
never have enough information to properly arrange many avian
groups in a definitive, evolutionary sequence.

4 MIGRATION AND NAVIGATION

Diversity is no less characteristic of the geographical movements of birds than of the anatomy and physiology of the avian body. There are some birds that tend to remain in essentially the same geographical area throughout the year and for as long as they survive. This is especially true of many tropical species and of some birds of temperate zones as well, such as the Great Horned Owl, Bobwhite Quail, and Cardinal, and these can be called sedentary species. But the majority of birds, and especially those in temperate latitudes, divide their time between two localities—one which they use for reproduction and a second which they use at those times when they are physiologically incapable of breeding. Since most birds breed but once a year, the movements between these two localities have an annual rhythm, and it is these rhythmic journeys, oriented between breeding area and non-breeding area, that we will consider in this discussion of migration. When we use the term "migration" in this restricted sense, we eliminate other types of movements such as emigrations, invasions, and erratic wanderings, which are biologically significant but do not relate to the problems to be discussed here.

Migrations are found in a number of different animal groups but are perhaps most conspicuous and best-defined among birds. The migration of birds aroused the interest and stimulated the imagination of mankind even prior to biblical times, but it was not until the late nineteenth century that there was general confirmation and appreciation of this widespread phenomenon. Aristotle and his contemporaries had a number of theories to account for the disappearance of birds at the onset of winter. Some species, like the swallows, were thought to overwinter in holes in the ground, while others were reported to undergo a transmutation into species that could withstand the rigors of

winter life. Thus, "*erithacus* (European Robin) and the so-
called redstart change into one another; the former is a winter
bird, the latter a summer one." Among the more incredible
theories regarding the ability of birds to hibernate is one proposed as late as the sixteenth century, which states that masses
of swallows form tight "balls" beneath the surface of ponds
where they pass the winter unless removed prematurely from
their hiding places by the nets of fishermen. Though hibernation
has now been eliminated as a common behavioral adaptation
among birds, we noted in the previous chapter that it has been
definitely established that at least some individuals of one
highly insectivorous species, the Poor-will of western North
America, hibernate as a means of avoiding the winter famine.

A bird's migratory behavior is as much an adaptation to its
environment as the structural modification of its bill or foot.
Since this behavioral adaptation is found in nearly all orders of
birds, it probably evolved independently during various periods
in evolution and in response to a number of different selective
processes. The result has been a variety of kinds of migrations
among birds today, each of which represents an adjustment
to a different set of environmental conditions. These annual
journeys are best developed in the colder, temperate regions
of the world, and especially in the northern hemisphere with
its large land masses and great climatic extremes. Nevertheless,
there are well-marked intertropical migrations, notably in Africa. In mountainous areas, as in western North America, there
are birds such as jays, chickadees, and juncos, that confine their
migrational movements to shifts in altitude that are synchronized with the changes in season. Migrations that are oriented
primarily in an east-west direction, as in the case of the California Gulls, are less common. Among the longest and most
spectacular migrations are those performed by oceanic species,
including some of the petrels and shearwaters (Fig. 29), that
twice annually make journeys of several thousand miles in
length.

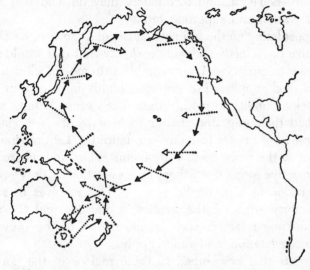

Fig. 29. The extraordinary migrations of the Short-tailed Shearwater. The breeding area is shown within the small, dotted circle; the migratory route is indicated by solid arrows. Note the direction of the prevailing winds along the route, indicated by dotted arrows. (After Marshall and Serventy.)

The Causes of Migration

One of the questions most frequently asked of an ornithologist is: "Why do birds migrate?" In seeking the causal factors of migration, it is helpful to think in terms of ultimate causes and proximate causes. The former are the historical reasons for migration that, through many generations of natural selection, have been incorporated into the genetic constitution of a bird. We can only speculate as to what these ultimate factors may have been, for it is impossible to substantiate these theories with experimentation. The proximate causes are those involving the present physical condition of the bird in relationship to its environment. What happens during each year to trigger migration? Twice annually these proximate causes initiate the migratory behavior, and fortunately they do lend themselves to observation and experimentation.

In speculating on the ultimate causes of migration, we should recognize the selective advantage of any trait that would allow a species to circumvent unfavorable extremes in climate and limited food supplies. For example, highly insectivorous birds that lack an ability to modify their diet seasonally must surely have had their migratory habits molded by the seasonal disappearance of insects in temperate latitudes. Less obvious is a solution to the more specific problem: When and where were such selective forces operating in the evolutionary development of migration in a particular species? This involves us in the evolutionary origin of the species in question and the many other unknown factors such as the nature of the prevailing climate, vegetation, and food supply.

Migrants that now breed in those regions of the northern hemisphere that were periodically covered with glaciers during the Pleistocene period may have evolved their migratory rhythms in one of two ways. Some birds of northern origin, such as the shrikes, may have sought refuge in the lower latitudes during glacial periods. After the ice receded, those that had successfully retreated before the ice may have returned to their former ranges in the north to breed, but continued to seek refuge farther south during subsequent winter seasons. Birds of subtropical origin, such as wood warblers and vireos, may have expanded their ranges northward following the retreat of the ice, thus taking advantage of spatial opportunities in the less congested temperate zones. Some of these pioneering forms influenced in this manner may have "returned home" after breeding due to a seasonal change in climate or food supply, thus completing the annual migratory rhythm (Fig. 30). This is not to deny, of course, that migrations may have and probably did exist prior to the Ice Age. It merely accounts for the tremendous influence that Pleistocene glaciation must have had upon migration patterns as we observe them today. The evolution of migratory patterns in areas uninfluenced by glaciation,

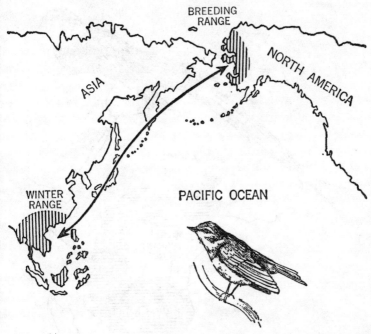

Fig. 30. The Alaska Willow Warbler is a race of an Asiatic species that has colonized western Alaska. Each year it migrates back through Asia to spend the winter in the Philippines and southeastern Asia; this migration evidently retraces the path by which the bird invaded Alaska.

as in the tropics, has in many instances been in response to seasonal changes which result in significant fluctuations in food supply (Fig. 31).

Migration and the Annual Cycle

Experimental investigations of the proximate factors in bird migration have been concerned with two major categories: (1) the intrinsic mechanisms (within the bird's body) that bring the bird into a state of physiological readiness for migratory flight, and (2) the extrinsic stimuli (received from the environment) for the actual release of migratory behavior. Migration,

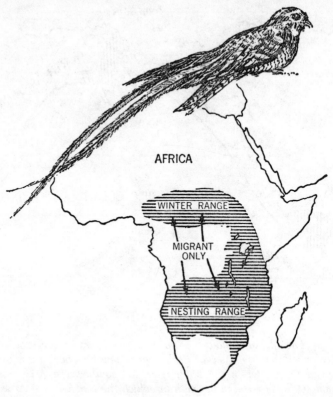

Fig. 31. The Pennant-winged Nightjar nests in the dry country south of the Congo forest and migrates across the forest to the dry savannas north of it. This migration is apparently regulated by the onset of the rainy season, which results in an abundance of insect food.

like reproduction and the molting and replacement of feathers, is but one phase of a complex, internal cycle of physiological events (Fig. 32). All phases of this annual cycle are closely dependent upon hormonal secretions of certain regulatory organs within the body, the endocrine glands.

With the completion of breeding activity, the endocrine glands most closely associated with reproduction (gonads) undergo regression and become unresponsive to external stimuli. It is usually during this period that the one complete molt of the

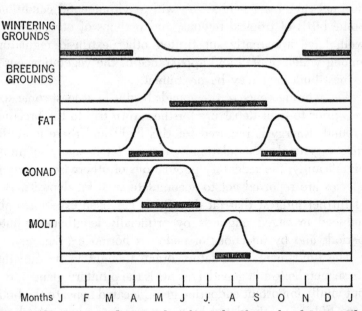

Fig. 32. The events in the annual cycle of the Slate-colored Junco. The time of migration is shown on the curves for wintering grounds and breeding grounds. (After Wolfson.)

plumage occurs, prior to the departure of migrants from their breeding ground. There are many exceptions to this rule, however. Some species of swallows and bee-eaters do not molt until after the migration. In other species, as in some tyrant flycatchers, the young birds may complete their molt prior to migration but the adults retain their worn feathers until after the journey.

A period of gradual resumption of gonadal activity follows the migration and complete molt, during which time the glands are once again responsive to extrinsic stimuli. In north temperate birds the increased gonadal activity generally begins in early fall, may be depressed or halted in winter, and speeds up once again under the influence of extrinsic stimuli in the spring. The seasonal appearance of specific and appropriate day lengths or photoperiods are believed to stimulate the nervous and endocrine systems of many species and thus help to keep their internal rhythms synchronized with environmental conditions. Some birds of tropical regions, and perhaps of other areas as well, have apparently substituted other extrinsic regulators, among which rainfall and appearance of the vegetation (used in nest-building) may be prominent.

The recrudescence of the gonads begins in at least some species prior to their departure for the return trip to the breeding ground. Energy is required for this flight and there is at this time a general accumulation of reserve fat in many migrants. Significantly, the sedentary populations of otherwise migratory species are reported not to accumulate such fat deposits. It is of further interest that fat deposition has been experimentally induced in caged migrants by artificially lengthened photoperiods and by injections of male sex hormone (Fig. 33).

The fundamental regulatory organ thought to be directing these metabolic and gonadal events is the pituitary gland, a tiny but vitally important endocrine gland located beneath the brain (see Fig. 17). Stimulated by an appropriate photoperiod and possibly other extrinsic factors, the pituitary influences the development of a metabolic state favorable for migration and at the same time stimulates the acceleration of gonadal activity in preparation for the breeding season. It has been suggested that the sex hormones have a direct influence upon migration, but the evidence is inconclusive and it would appear that both the recrudescence of the gonads and migration behavior are themselves manifestations of increased pituitary activity. Undoubtedly the thyroid gland also plays a vital role in this physiological cycle, but its contribution remains speculative at this time. We have already noted that in the tropics, where variation in day length is too slight to be effective, other environmental stimuli presumably replace photoperiodism as the key to the synchronization of the internal physiological rhythm with the environment. The actual initiation of the migratory journey can be attributed to the influence of certain environmental stimuli, such as favorable temperatures, winds, and atmospheric condi-

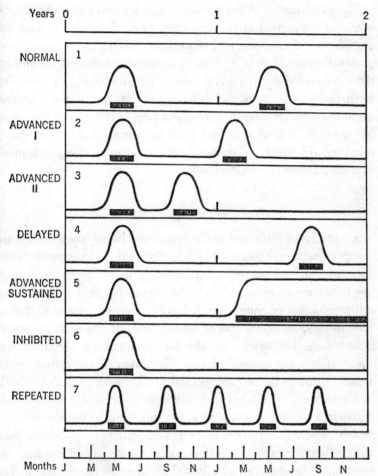

Fig. 33. Modifications in the reproductive cycle of the Slate-colored Junco, induced experimentally through manipulation of the photoperiod. (After Wolfson.)

tions, upon a bird that is physiologically ready and capable of making such a journey.

The culmination of the period of accelerated gonadal activity occurs after arrival at the breeding ground and is marked by completion of the nest and mating act itself. These events are under direct control of various environmental stimuli, including those provided by the mate, nest site, and nesting materials. Both the acceleration and culmination phases of the gonadal cycle may be influenced by temperature. If it is unusually cold, for example, sexual processes may be retarded. In the tropics, rain probably plays a significant role in bringing about culmination of reproductive activity.

Methods of Studying Migration

A variety of different techniques are being used today to observe and study migrating birds. Some of these provide valuable information on migration actually in progress, including the influence of geographical and meteorological factors, and the mechanics of migratory behavior such as speed, altitude, time of day, and direction of flights. Two of the more recently introduced techniques merit special mention here. One involves observations and counts of the silhouettes of migrating birds as seen through telescopes focused on the moon. Data obtained by these lunar counts, as they are called, provide more precise numerical measurements and approximations of the directional trends of mass migration movements than heretofore possible with other visual observation techniques. Lunar counts, of course, are limited to but a few days of each month when the moon is full and skies are clear. More recently, our ability to "observe" migrations has been greatly extended by the realization that large birds and groups of smaller migrants register themselves on radar screens. These responses on the radarscope, called "angels" because formerly their source was unknown, are of particular value in correlating migratory movements with geographical and meteorological factors over extensive land areas.

No single technique has contributed as much to our understanding of avian migration as has the practice of banding or otherwise marking birds to permit their individual identification when subsequently recovered. Most commonly, a metallic band of aluminum or copper-base alloy is placed around the bird's leg, bearing a distinctive number and an address to which the report of the recovery may be sent. These bands come in various sizes designed for everything from hummingbirds to swans. Special tags have been designed for use on the flippers of penguins, and bands and tags of distinctive colors and shapes are sometimes used to permit the individual identification of birds at a distance, without the necessity of actually recovering them. Outstanding banding programs, with large networks of active banders, are now established in many countries. Bird banding in North America is under the general direction of the U. S. Fish and Wildlife Service and the Canadian Wildlife Service, with participation by state and provincial game departments and some 2000 licensed and qualified volunteers. This cooperative effort has resulted in the banding of over 11 million individuals of about 600 species of North American birds since 1920, with some 600,000 new birds banded yearly.

Birds are banded or marked either as young in the nest or as adults that have been trapped by any of a variety of methods. The chances of obtaining subsequent information on a banded bird vary greatly with the species and the circumstances under which it was banded. In the case of waterfowl, where hunting practices increase the prospect of recovery, subsequent information may possibly be forthcoming on as many as 10 to 20 per cent of the birds that have been banded. Of song birds banded during migration, on the other hand, less than 1 per cent are usually recovered. If, however, song birds are banded on their breeding ground, subsequent attempts to find them at the banding locality have been known to run as high as 60 per cent recovery or more.

Characteristics of Migration

The routes followed by migrating birds are in a general way determined by a line drawn between the breeding ground and non-breeding area. Deviations from these shortest possible routes may develop due to local weather conditions, and especially to topographic features such as seacoasts, mountain ranges, and waterways. Though the route followed by the entire species may be geographically broad, coincident with a widespread distribution of its member populations, individual birds probably follow rather narrow and well-prescribed migration routes year after year. In a few cases, the route followed on the way to the breeding ground is quite distinct from the one taken away from the breeding ground (Fig. 34).

Some of these journeys are made essentially nonstop, requiring tremendous expenditures of energy. Land birds flying from Scandinavia to Great Britain must fly over 200 to 400 miles of water, and many land migrants regularly make the 600-mile flight across the Gulf of Mexico. Golden Plovers and other shorebirds are believed to fly nonstop over the 2000 miles of ocean separating the Aleutian Islands from Hawaii. The majority of birds migrating over land, however, stop at intervals to feed and rest and perhaps average only 100 miles in a day. The rate of progress of this type of migration is often linked with temperature and atmospheric conditions, but may accelerate as the birds approach their goal (Fig. 35). In the north temperate latitudes there is evidence that early spring migrants are more readily influenced by weather than those that migrate later in the spring. But at all times, migrants seem to move when favorable atmospheric conditions prevail. In eastern North America, for example, pronounced movements of spring migrants take place into or through a given region during the interval between the passage of a warm front through that region and the subsequent arrival of a cold front. Lunar and radar studies suggest

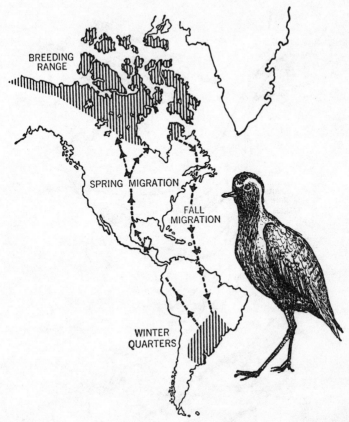

Fig. 34. The Eastern Golden Plover in spring migrates up the Mississippi Valley, at which season the Canadian and Labrador coasts are still cold and barren. In the autumn, however, it migrates down the Atlantic coast, first stopping in Labrador where it becomes fat from foraging on crowberries, and then proceeding by non-stop flight to the northern coast of South America. It then continues to its winter grounds on the pampas of Argentina.

that night migrants may also use such a system of pressure-pattern flying.

We know that some migrating birds, such as ducks and geese, regularly cross mountain ranges in excess of 15,000 feet, and therefore must be physiologically capable of flight at this ex-

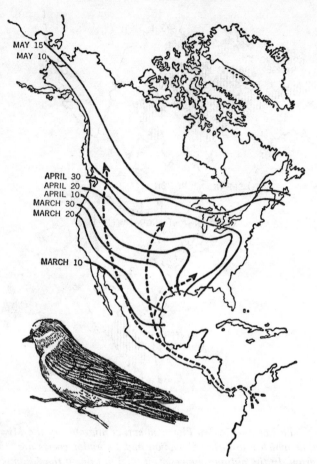

Fig. 35. The Cliff Swallow migrates by day, feeding on the wing as it goes. It progresses at a relatively steady rate (pace) and, unlike some night migrants, does not fly across the Gulf of Mexico but goes around it.

treme altitude. In general, however, migration usually proceeds at moderate heights, with few species consistently flying above 5000 feet and the majority perhaps remaining below 3000 feet. The altitude of flight, as well as the forward progress, is apparently modified by atmospheric conditions, especially wind.

Birds differ with respect to the time of day used for migration movements. Some species, like the swallows, hawks, and some of the finches, travel largely during the daylight hours, while the warblers, thrushes, vireos, and others travel mostly at night. Radar and lunar studies suggest that nocturnal migration reaches a peak of activity just before midnight, followed by a pronounced decline. The bright lights of airport ceilometers, radio towers, lighthouses, and other tall buildings all too often attract or confuse these night migrants to the extent that the toll of casualties is staggering. At an airport in Georgia, over 50,000 birds are known to have been killed in a single night. But migration losses due to natural causes, such as severe storms, probably far exceed the fatalities attributable to man.

Homing Ability

How birds navigate during migration is one of the most perplexing problems in all biology. That they possess this ability is based on an overwhelming accumulation of banding and experimental evidence. Species that annually journey to geographically restricted "goals" clearly demonstrate this phenomenal attribute. Though the Greater Shearwater, for example, ranges over nearly all of the Atlantic Ocean, individuals journeying to their breeding ground must pinpoint their flight to the islands of the Tristan da Cunha group, which spread over only 150 square miles of the South Atlantic and lie 1500 miles from the nearest land mass. The entire population of the Kirtland Warbler is known to nest only in one restricted area of Michigan, less than 85 miles wide and 100 miles long, and winters exclusively in the Bahama Islands. This 1200-mile journey demands some extraordinary homing ability twice each year. Banding studies further suggest that it is probably the rule rather than the exception that individuals of most species of birds habitually return to the same breeding ground and the same "wintering" ground year after year, often to the same few acres of land.

It seems apparent as a result of a number of experimental

approaches that at least part of this navigational success of
birds is due to a reliance on visual clues or landmarks. The speed
of return and the per cent returns of birds experimentally displaced from their nests are invariably greater when these
experiments are conducted in an area familiar to the birds.
One significant series of experiments involved the following of
displaced birds with an airplane and the mapping of the routes
used by each bird in returning to its nest. Though many of these
birds were ultimately successful in reaching home, they invariably did not orient immediately toward home but first spent
considerable time in exploratory flight within the unfamiliar
region of release. We know from efforts made to establish birds
in previously uncolonized areas, by removing eggs to some new
area and having them hatch there, that the birds have rather
consistently returned to the site where they were hatched rather
than to the locality where the eggs were laid. These experiments
have generally been successful if performed prior to the first fall
molt, but not thereafter, implying that the attachment to a
particular site is based upon impressions that the young birds
receive from their environment between the time of hatching
and their first migration.

It seems likely that recognition of familiar landmarks is involved in the orientation of birds to both their breeding ground
and "wintering" area. A bird returning to its nesting territory
in the spring need only use an exploratory search pattern until
it finds a familiar point within the perimeter of known territory,
which may be rather extensive. We have seen how birds have
a very well-developed mechanism for visual perception, and
psychological studies have indicated an equally remarkable visual memory. Thus, it is not unlikely that they can retain mem-
ories of specific visual landmarks. As might be expected when
nonmigratory species are used in displacement experiments,
they show little or no homing ability when taken more than a
few miles from familiar territory.

But information from a number of other sources makes it
equally apparent that at least some species of birds possess a

"compass sense" in addition to the comparatively simple mechanism of recognition of visual landmarks. We have innumerable observations of the remarkable homing ability of birds that have been experimentally displaced great distances from their nests, necessitating flights over completely unfamiliar geography. In one such experiment 18 Laysan Albatrosses were taken from their nests on Midway Island and flown by airplane to different locations around the Pacific. Fourteen of these birds returned successfully, and one was back on its nest 32 days after its release in the Philippines, some 4120 miles away and well beyond the normal range of the species. In still another remarkable experiment, a Manx Shearwater that had been flown from its nest burrow in England to Boston, a distance of over 3000 miles, was back in its burrow in England 12 days later.

The Basis for Orientation

During the last two decades there has been a considerable effort among experimental biologists to find a solution to this mystery, and a plethora of ingenious theories have been presented. It has been postulated, for example, that a flying bird might be receptive to the mechanical forces resulting from the earth's rotation, possibly through slight changes in body weight or pressures upon blood flowing through the arteries. Since this effect would be zero at the geographical poles and greatest at the equator, the bird could presumably use these forces to determine its latitudinal position. Sensitivity to the vertical component of the earth's magnetic field, which varies according to the distance from the magnetic poles, could then theoretically be used to establish longitudinal position. Other workers have suggested that birds perform their annual journeys by means of infrared vision, enabling them to detect long wave radiation emanating from the warmer parts of the earth. Most of these theories, though provocative and stimulating when first introduced, have not been supported by repeated and critical experimentation. All propose a degree of sensory perception far in excess of the capacity of any known biological mechanism.

A breakthrough in our efforts to better understand the mystery of bird migration came with a series of reports published in the early 1950's of experiments performed in Germany. Capitalizing on the well-known phenomenon of restlessness among caged birds during the migration period, these scientists were able to establish that the birds orient themselves within their cages in a direction corresponding to that normally taken by migrating individuals of the same species in the wild. Of paramount significance was their observation that the caged birds performed best under a clear sky and became generally disoriented when there was a heavy overcast. If the apparent direction of the sunlight was shifted with mirrors, the birds shifted the direction of their restless activity accordingly. These experiments were repeated many times and the results consistently and clearly demonstrated that at least some species of birds, including the European Starling and Western Meadowlark, utilize clues from the sky in determining orientation of migratory activity. These findings based on caged birds gave added significance to prior observations made in field experiments that birds generally perform better under clear skies when homing over unfamiliar territory. Subsequent investigations indicated that direct sunlight was not essential for proper orientation, and that only the opportunity to correctly establish the sun's position was required. Whether the intensity or some physical quality of sunlight provides additional clues is not clear. Some insects, bees for example, will respond to the polarization of light and hence are able to orient on the basis of clues emanating from a relatively small patch of blue sky. But birds appear not to be receptive to polarized light.

Further insight into the ability of birds to use celestial clues for purposes of orientation has been obtained by training caged Starlings and other species to seek food in a particular compass direction. In this training procedure, birds were conditioned to orient in a specific direction and at the same time each day, with food as the reward. The methods used eliminated the possibility that the birds might be using visible landmarks other than the sun (Fig. 36). Subsequent tests, conducted at times when the sun's position was different from that in the training period, demonstrated that some birds were able to correct for the time

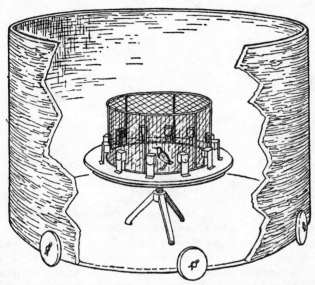

Fig. 36. A training cage used in orientation experiments. A circular masonite wall excludes landmarks from the bird's vision. The twelve feeders (shown here covered) can be uncovered simultaneously by revolving the movable ring. (After von Saint Paul.)

of day and choose the proper compass direction (Fig. 37). We now have other corroborative evidence that a number of species do possess some sort of "internal clock" whereby they are able to take the sun's position into account and make a time correction for its passage across the sky. Of particular interest is the fact that some of the species in which this ability has been demonstrated are principally nocturnal migrants, including the Barred Warbler and Red-backed Shrike. Sun orientation has now been reported in a variety of other animals, including several insects, fish, and reptiles.

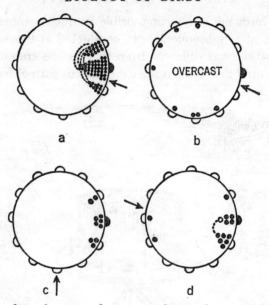

Fig. 37. In these diagrams, the arrow indicates the position of the sun and each semicircle on the circumference indicates the location of a feeder, the black semicircle being the one the bird was trained to. Black dots represent first choices made by the bird; white dots are second choices. In (a), the meadowlark was trained to seek food from the east feeder between 7:50 and 8:00 A.M. When the feeder was opened during a period of overcast at 8:00 A.M. (b), the bird became completely disoriented. In (c), the feeder was opened at noon and the bird continued to show general orientation to the east feeder. When the feeder was opened at 5:50 P.M. (d), the bird's orientation was markedly to the east feeder although the sun was in the west. (After von Saint Paul.)

On the basis of these studies with caged birds, it is logical to suppose that migrating birds might well use the sun as a compass to enable them to find and maintain their proper orientation. But there is something else needed. In the case of the remarkable homing performances of experimentally displaced birds, for example, how were these birds able to determine the relationship between the point of release and their goal? If they were to rely solely upon sun orientation or direction-finding, it is doubtful that they would ever reach their goal unless displaced in the appropriate direction. Could the sun also be providing clues that would allow for a system of bicoordinate navigation, i.e., a means of determining position as well as direction? One scientist has advanced just such a theory of sun navigation, based on an ability of the bird to determine its position by visual estimation of the altitude of the sun above the horizon, the rate of change of this altitude, plus an awareness of the approximate time of day. Though theoretically sound, this sun navigation hypothesis would seem to demand a great deal of the bird's sensory capacities as we currently understand them, and there is as yet no conclusive experimental evidence in its favor.

Navigation by the Stars

A second breakthrough in research on bird navigation came in 1956 with reports of observations and experiments involving caged European warblers under the night sky. Migratory restlessness of each species was observed to be oriented in the compass direction toward which that species normally starts its migration from central Europe to Africa, though the birds could see nothing of their surroundings but the sky above them. Even inexperienced individuals that had been hatched and hand-raised in isolation chambers were able to orient in the appropriate direction, providing they had access to the night sky. When the stars were hidden by thick clouds, however, the birds invariably became disoriented.

A series of ingenious experiments were then performed with these same warblers in a planetarium, under various artificial skies. When the dome of the planetarium was merely illuminated with diffuse light and no stars, there was no consistent directionality to the warblers' restlessness. But when the dome presented a replica of the night sky over Europe, the birds oriented as they had done in the outdoor cages. These experiments indicated that it is possible for nocturnal migrants to use the stars for direction-finding, just as diurnal migrants are able to use the sun. To determine whether or not the stars provide clues for bicoordinate navigation, the planetarium "sky" was altered to correspond to other latitudes along the usual migration route of these birds. The caged birds were then observed to alter their direction of activity to correspond to the direction they would normally follow at those latitudes. In another series of tests an inexperienced warbler was exposed to shifts in the planetarium sky which effectively changed its longitudinal position from the usual migration starting point in Germany to a point in Siberia. It was initially disoriented but then redirected its restlessness toward the west. As the "sky" was gradually shifted back to the starry configuration over Germany, the bird oriented more and more toward the south and its normal migratory direction. In other words, these birds appeared to be using the sky for determining the latitude and longitude of their displaced positions and hence demonstrated true navigation (Fig. 38). It has been suggested that the birds may actually recognize and evaluate the geometrical arrangements of the stars, or constellations, and use their azimuth and altitude to establish a grid of coordination. But as in the case of navigation by the sun, the actual mechanism of navigation by the stars remains obscure.

Thus, we still do not have the complete answer to the age-old problem of how migrating birds find their way. That the sun and stars provide useful navigational clues has now been established. The exact nature of these clues, how they are perceived, and how they are translated by migrating birds remain fruitful areas of research. There is the possibility, of course, that birds possess a distinctly different means of navigation still unknown to science.

Since most of the experimental work thus far has been with caged birds, there is a need for more data on the behavior of free-flying migratory birds. Recent advancements in electronic instrumentation may provide this information, for serious consideration is now being given to the placement of miniature radio transmitters on migrating birds. Tiny photo cells may

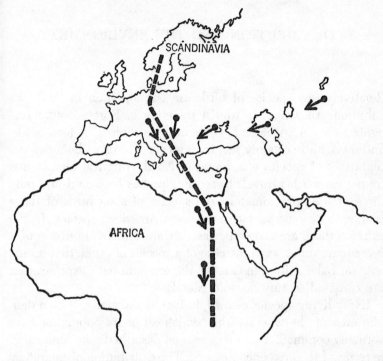

Fig. 38. The dotted black line shows the migratory path of the Lesser Whitethroat. The arrows show the directions taken by the warbler in the planetarium experiment when the planetarium sky was adjusted to correspond to the sky as it would appear over each point on the map. (After Sauer.)

also be incorporated in the instrument package to tell the scientists whether or not the sun is visible to the bird. Such data would then be correlated with flight and homing performances. These telemetering devices would, of course, have to be small enough and light enough so as not to interfere with normal flight behavior. Another breakthrough in this fascinating research on avian navigation may be imminent.

5 DISTRIBUTION AND THE ENVIRONMENT

Relatively few species of birds are cosmopolitan in their distribution. An American tourist traveling in Europe might recognize several species of water and shorebirds, a few hawks and owls, and certainly less than 20 song birds as being representatives of species also found in North America. Should this tourist extend his travels to the Philippines he would find only three of the approximately 180 species of song birds of those islands to be representative of North American species. In the extreme there are those species that are unknown outside of a few square miles, as in the case of a species of grebe that occurs only on Lake Atitlán in Guatemala, or a number of species that are confined to tiny oceanic islands.

Every living species of bird, in fact, is associated with a definite area of the world within which all of its populations are normally confined. This range can be described *geographically*, in terms of the area encompassed. The distribution of migratory species can be further designated in geographical terms according to the breeding range, non-breeding range, and migratory route followed. Another way of describing the distribution of a given species is in terms of the interrelationships between the bird and its environment. The division of biology devoted to the study of these relationships is called *ecology*. Few species are uniformly distributed throughout their geographic ranges but are instead characteristically associated with particular types of environment or habitat. The Long-billed Marsh Wren, for example, has a breeding range that extends over most of southern Canada and the entire United States. Within this geographical range, however, its distribution is extremely spotty, for its breeding populations are ecologically restricted to marshy habitats. Why isn't this species represented in equally suitable marsh environments in Europe or Asia? In this chapter we shall consider some of the historical and ecological factors that have been influential in determining the present distribution of birds, including the role played by man himself.

Historical Distribution

In seeking an explanation for birds being distributed as we see them today, we must first consider the historical factors involved. The origin of the group to which a particular species belongs is of obvious importance in the present distribution of that species. The Long-billed Marsh Wren, noted above, is clearly a member of a well-defined family of birds, the wrens (Troglodytidae). All but one of the 63 species of wrens are confined to the New World, and it seems logical to conclude that the group originated there and has shown little evidence of dispersal elsewhere. There are a number of comparatively recent evolutionary groups with restricted ranges which lend themselves to this kind of analysis, including the New World flycatchers (Tyrannidae) and blackbirds and orioles (Icteridae).

Unfortunately for the avian zoogeographer, the evidence for the origin and subsequent dispersal routes of many birds is not this conclusive. In the first place, as we have already noted, the fossil record for birds is poor and it is only in few instances that we can be sure of the place of origin of the widely distributed families. In the second place, remarkable potential for adaptation, a warm-blooded physiology, and especially the power of flight have enabled birds to far surpass other vertebrates in their ability to reach, and take advantage of, new environments. Most of the remote islands of the world, for example, have been colonized by land birds. All too often this dispersal has been too rapid to trace. Migratory behavior has further complicated patterns of distribution, especially by speeding up the merger of tropical and temperate bird faunas in both the Old and New Worlds.

The complex process of the evolution of the major groups

of birds—their adaptive radiation, dispersal, and subsequent retreat and intermittent extinction—has been controlled largely
by climatological events and effective geographical barriers.
We noted in the first chapter that most if not all of the modern
families of birds had come into being by the early Tertiary
period (see Fig. 4), some 60 million years ago. Consequently,
the conditions prevalent during this period must have had pro-
found influences on distributional patterns as we know them
today. Geologists tell us that the configuration and location of
the great continental land masses of the Tertiary were essentially as we know them now, but throughout this period, there
were marked changes in the surface contours and in the land
connections between continents. For example, a land bridge between Asia and North America, across the Bering Strait, was
probably formed and broken several times. Old World families,
such as the shrikes and the larks, crossed it into North America,
while North American species, including one species of wren,
crossed into Asia. Similarly, North and South America were
separated at the beginning of the Tertiary by ocean gaps in
Central America. Some families developed north of the gap,
some south of it, and many genera and species still reach
their northern or southern limit in the Panama region. For example, the Hairy Woodpecker and the Brown Jay are found
only to the north of Panama, while Swainson's Antcatcher and
the Black-backed Ant Shrike, are found only to the south. Also,
in the early Tertiary subtropical vegetation occurred further
north, into the present temperate zones. Such changes in climate and land connections encouraged an intercontinental exchange of certain groups which serves to obscure their origin.

The climate of the Tertiary gradually cooled, culminating
about one million years ago in the first of the Pleistocene glaciations. There were four successive advances of the arctic glaciers
into temperate zones, the last of which retreated a mere
10,000 years ago. Between these glaciations, however, climates
were thought to have been not unlike that of today, and it may
well be that our current post-Pleistocene period is but another

of these interglacials. Such remarkable cyclic fluctuations in extremes of climate and associated vegetation must certainly have caused a comparable fluctuation in the distribution of birds of the north temperate latitudes. Furthermore, the periodic lowering of sea level associated with each of the glaciations may have activated land bridges between continents and also permitted continental land birds to colonize many of the outlying islands. The British Isles, for example, were once connected with Europe, and their birdlife is quite similar to that of western Europe. The rather numerous differences that do exist are explained by the fact that the English Channel appeared near the close of the last glacial period while the British Isles were still partly covered with ice and were unsuitable for many species of birds. Some species, such as the Great Black Woodpecker and the Medium Spotted Woodpecker, occur on the continent but have not crossed the channel to the British Isles. On the other hand, the Greater Spotted Woodpecker and the Wood Lark crossed from the continent to England, but the channel between England and Ireland has kept them from colonizing Ireland. The Skylark and the European Robin, however, have crossed both channels and occur throughout the British Isles.

The Faunal Regions of the World

Throughout both the Tertiary and Pleistocene, when the avenues for potential intercontinental exchange of land bird faunas were periodically opened and closed by geological and climatological events, the rate and extent of dispersal of birds from their centers of origin were not uniform for all groups and in all directions. Some birds were stopped by water gaps and climatological barriers, while others crossed these barriers at different times and for different distances. Consequently, today, we are able to recognize a number of faunal or zoogeographical regions of the world which represent the average, gross pattern of distribution of many different land birds having more or less different individual distributions (Fig. 39). The birds in differ-

Fig. 39. The zoogeographical regions of the world.

ent parts of any one of these faunal regions are generally more related to those of other parts of the same region than to the birds of other regions. Though some uniformity prevails throughout a given region, each of the regional faunas enters into complex transitions with the adjacent faunas.

The whole of Africa south of the Sahara Desert has been designated by zoogeographers as the Ethiopian Region, while tropical Asia south of the Himalayas and southern China constitutes the Oriental Region. These two extensive land areas share many major groups of birds, reflecting their closer union during the Tertiary. Among these are the bee-eaters (Meropidae), sunbirds (Nectariniidae), hornbills (Bucerotidae), and babblers (Timaliidae). That there has been considerable independent evolution since then is suggested by the fact that only 2 per cent of the Ethiopian birds, *at the species level*, are to be found in the Oriental Region as well (Fig. 40). Only a few *families* of birds are unique or endemic to the Ethiopian and Oriental faunas, for there has been an extensive northward dispersal by representatives of most groups. These bird faunas of the Old World tropics are generally considered to have been

Fig. 40. Birds characteristic of the Ethiopian (a, b) and Oriental (c, d) regions: (a) guinea hen, (b) touraco, (c) bamboo partridge, (d) babbler.

the great reservoirs for avian evolution and the major dispersal centers during the late Cretaceous and early Tertiary times. Characteristic families of the Ethiopian Region include the guinea fowls (Numididae), Ostriches (Struthionidae), colies or mousebirds (Coliidae), and the touracos (Musophagidae). The fairy bluebirds perhaps comprise the only family (Irenidae) endemic to the Oriental Region.

The land bird faunas of the temperate and cold regions of the Old World, the Palearctic, and of the New World, the Nearctic, have been described as depauperate fringe areas of the far richer tropical faunas. Both of these areas, sometimes collectively referred to as the Holarctic, are characterized by fewer species and by extensive annual migrations of birds during the northern winter. There is but one family of birds restricted to the Palearctic, the hedge sparrows (Prunellidae), and there are few, if any, avian families endemic to the Nearctic, for nearly all are shared to some degree with adjacent faunas or transitional zones. As we have seen, the Bering Strait has functioned successfully as an avenue of exchange for many land birds of the Palearctic and Nearctic faunas, though these dispersal movements have not been equal in both directions. There are many avian families of temperate Eurasia which now have representatives in North America, but there are comparatively few birds of North American origin that have spread into the Old World. Many groups of less than family rank have evolved independently in each of these regions, however, and the two subdivisions of the Holarctic are further differentiated on the basis of the elements that each has derived from its adjacent tropical fauna.

The richest of the zoogeographical regions, in terms of the number and diversity of its bird species, is the Neotropical, which includes South America, Central America northward to southern Mexico, and the West Indies. This diversity, characterized by the largest concentration of endemic families of any region of the world, has been interpreted as representing extensive secondary differentiation of pioneering elements re-

ceived from Eurasia and North America. Some of these successful groups, almost certainly of Neotropical origin, have since
extended their ranges into the Nearctic (vireos, wood warblers,
blackbirds and orioles, tyrant flycatchers, and tanagers). With
one or two notable exceptions, none have been able to penetrate
into the Palearctic Region, however. Among the many endemic
groups are the manakins, cotingas, ovenbirds, and antbirds. The
Neotropical Region, being far removed from the presumed primary centers of radiation in the Old World tropics, has apparently never been colonized by a number of widespread
groups of birds, including the cranes, hornbills, titmice, and
shrikes (Fig. 41).

The Australian Region differs from the other faunal areas,
historically, in never having had land connections with adjacent continents throughout the Tertiary or Pleistocene. Like
South America, it represents a "blind alley" in terms of avenues
or corridors for the dispersal of land birds. Geographically it
includes New Guinea, New Zealand, and the Polynesian islands,
as well as the continent of Australia. The affinities of its bird
fauna are unmistakably with the avifauna of Asia, and most of
the wide-ranging Old World families are represented. Colonization must have occurred by island-hopping, early in the Tertiary, followed by considerable secondary differentiation that
has resulted in an array of endemic families second in number
only to the Neotropical Region. Typical avian families of the
Australian Region include the emus, kiwis, mound builders,
lyre-birds, and birds of paradise. Additional families, like the
wood swallows, flowerpeckers, and frogmouths, are shared only
with the adjacent Oriental Region.

Among the most puzzling problems inherent in any attempt
to reconstruct the origin and subsequent dispersal routes of the
birds of the world are those presented by the families of birds
that have a pantropical distribution, i.e., occur only in tropical climate and are represented both in the Old World and New
World tropics. Such a discontinuous distribution might con-

Fig. 41. Birds characteristic of the Neotropical (a, b) and Australian (c, d) regions: (a) toucan, (b) cotinga, (c) lory, (d) bell-magpie.

ceivably have been achieved by means of transoceanic colonization in the case of certain pantropical ducks, but some other explanation must be sought for land birds like the barbets, parrots, and trogons. One theory that has been postulated is that the presently distributed continents were formerly grouped into but two great land masses, one of which would have included most of the tropical areas of present continents and hence could have accounted for the pantropical distribution of some of the present-day land fauna. Later these land masses fragmented and subsequently drifted to their present positions. But geologists tell us that if this drifting of continents occurred at all, it must have been prior to the major dispersal movements of birds in the early Tertiary. Furthermore, if such land connections had in fact been utilized by tropical birds, why wasn't a more complete exchange of bird (and other animal) faunas effected by the same means? An alternative explanation for this exchange of tropical faunas would be the use of the Bering Strait bridge, implying a far greater distribution than now occurs. Indeed, fossil trogons from Europe are evidence of a range retreat in that tropical group. Yet it is doubtful that conditions at the Bering Strait were ever favorable for strictly tropical faunas, even during the warmest portion of the Tertiary. Conceivably the exchanges could have been effected by former representatives of these tropical families that were better adapted for temperate environments. No completely satisfactory solution has yet been found.

Marine faunas, like the continental faunas, have experienced expansion and retreat movements in tune with climatic cycles during the Tertiary and Pleistocene, though on a much reduced scale. Principal factors influencing the distribution of marine birds would appear to be the occurrence and availability of food and the presence of terrestrial nesting sites. Although various parts of the oceans may appear similar to us, definite areas exist that differ from one another in water temperature, salinity, and other factors, including the quantity of fish and other available food. Ocean currents have a marked effect on the distribution of these oceanic life zones (Fig. 42). The bird fauna is broadly uniform throughout each of these life zones, but pronounced differences are to be observed when one crosses the boundaries or convergences between the zones. Penguins are the most distinctive birds of the southern marine region, while the auks are their ecological counterparts in the northern marine region. Between these two zones is the tropical marine region, characterized by species of boobies and tropic-birds.

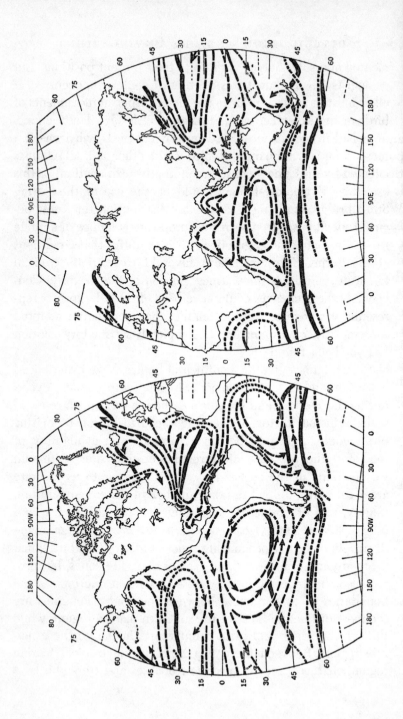

The Role of Environment

We have seen that historical factors, such as place of origin and potential avenues for dispersal, have been of primary importance in governing the gross aspects of avian distribution through the world. Knowing that the Long-billed Marsh Wren is a member of a family of birds of comparatively recent New World origin helps to explain its present restriction to the Nearctic Region. That this species has not found environmental conditions favorable for dispersal beyond the limits of its present distribution suggests the influence of additional factors, namely, the interrelationships between the wren and its environment. A bird's environment, or more specifically its habitat, consists of the physical and biological conditions that surround it, including other birds that might possibly be competing for similar resources. In order to live successfully in a particular habitat, a bird must be physiologically and morphologically adapted to that habitat. It is difficult to imagine, for example, that a jacana, with its peculiar feet, could survive in an arboreal habitat in competition with chickadees and vireos. And how successful would the nectar-feeding hummingbirds and honey-eaters be in a habitat with no flowering plants? If we further consider the special behavioral patterns that the bird has evolved to better utilize these structural adaptations, we introduce the concept of the ecological niche—the particular position occupied by the bird within its habitat (Fig. 43). A consideration of some of these ecological factors will help to explain why most birds are not distributed uniformly throughout their entire geo-

---

Fig. 42. Ocean currents have a marked effect on the distribution of the oceanic life zones. The dashed arrows are warm currents, the dotted arrows cold currents. The solid lines nearest the equator mark the subtropical convergences (the limits of warm-temperate waters), while those in high latitudes mark the Arctic and Antarctic convergences (the limits of the polar seas). Along these convergences, ocean surface waters of different physical characteristics meet.

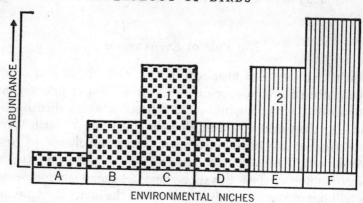

Fig. 43. Species 1 finds optimal conditions in niche C and reaches greatest abundance in that niche. It can also utilize niches B and D with less efficiency, and A very poorly. Species 2 cannot use A, B, and C, but finds D partially suitable, E and especially F very suitable. Species 1 and 2 overlap in niche D but species 2 prevents any occupancy of niche E by species 1. (After Mayr.)

graphical range and why their geographical ranges are contained as they are.

One of the obvious trends in the evolution of birds has been an increasing diversity in the types of ecological niches which they are able to occupy, thus permitting a more efficient utilization of all resources of the environment. Species vary, however, in their ecological tolerances, i.e., the degree to which they are restricted to a single habitat and niche, and these tolerances are in turn reflected in their distribution. Those that are adapted for a relatively specialized way of life may be correspondingly confined in their distribution. The distribution of crossbills, birds adapted for extracting seeds from the cones of trees, coincides closely, as one would expect, with the distribution of the coniferous forest, and these birds have been known to abandon a portion of their breeding range when the supply of these cones has been exhausted. In cases of extreme specialization and where birds are unable to adapt to alterations in their environment, extinction is invariably the consequence. Ivory-billed Woodpeckers, dependent upon large trees in wilderness areas of North America for nest sites and appropriate food, have experienced drastic reductions in their distribution and population size which places them on the brink of extinction. But many species have extremely broad ecological tolerances and are remarkably ubiquitous in their distribution. The Mourning Dove, for example, is to be found throughout most open or semi-open habitats within its geographical range, and populations are to be found in the deserts in Arizona, the prairies of Iowa, urban developments in New York City, and in clearings within the coniferous forest of Alaska.

Major Habitats of the World

That the geographical range of a species frequently coincides with the distribution of a particular type of habitat is an indication of the influence of a whole complex of physical and biological factors that distinguishes that habitat from adjacent ones. Seldom is it possible to single out one of these environmental attributes as being *the* limiting factor in containing the species within its present range. But most birds are dependent, either directly or indirectly, upon the vegetation that characterizes their habitat, for this vital resource may provide food, shelter, escape from predators, and building material for their nests. Because of this dependency, it is possible to further analyze the distribution of birds according to a classification of the major types of habitat throughout the world based upon the gross structure or physiognomy of the vegetation.

There are certain "indicator species" of birds which are conspicuously and almost exclusively associated with each of these major environmental communities. When one of these habitats is represented in two or more of the zoogeographical regions, as is often the case, its indicator species will usually differ taxonomically but will be similar in their ecological requirements. When these unrelated species occupy the same niche within a particular type of community, but in separate parts of

the world, they are regarded as ecological equivalents and are
products of evolutionary convergence (Fig. 44). In considering
a few of these major habitats, we will identify some of the in
dicator species and suggest possible physical and biological fac
tors that may be of importance to these birds.

The deserts and savannas of the world, characterized by their

*Fig. 44. Ecological equivalents: the meadowlark of North America
(below) and the Yellow-throated Long Claw of East Africa. Both occu
in similar habitats, both nest in long grass, both are similarly marked, with
a yellow throat and a dark V on the chest. (The Yellow-throated Long
Claw after van Someren.)*

low, sparse, and often thorny vegetation, impose a number of critical conditions upon their birdlife—extremes of diurnal and seasonal temperature, low annual rainfall, and frequently strong winds (Fig. 45). Birds, with their great mobility, are better able to reach distant water sources than most animals, yet desert birds are often dependent upon additional adaptations for water economy, which may involve reliance upon highly succulent animal and vegetable foods or a capacity to hold large quantities of water in the digestive tract. The Burrowing Owl of the New World and representatives of at least three other orders of birds make use of the burrows of rodents for both nest sites and shelter from the heat and strong winds. The openness of arid lands has led to the development of cursorial habits among certain species, like the Roadrunner of southwestern North America which depends upon its great speed for capturing quick-moving lizards. Speed in running reaches its extreme development among birds of the savannas such as the Ostrich and rhea, at the cost of flight. Plumage coloration is predominantly pallid in birds of arid and semi-arid regions, and this is most evident in the desert representatives of those species which also have populations living in more humid climates (see Fig. 22).

Those portions of the far north which are not perpetually covered with ice and snow have a physiognomy somewhat similar to that of the deserts and savannas, though the vegetation consists principally of sedges, lichens, mosses, and dwarf trees (see Fig. 45). Birds of the tundra, as this habitat is called, have no problem of water economy, since following the spring thaw the soil is soggy and there are numerous depressions with standing water. While extremely low winter temperatures and frozen soil and ponds force the majority of the tundra species to migrate, dense plumages and fat deposits enable a few species to remain on the tundra the year around. The feathered tarsi of the Gyrfalcon (Fig. 46) are an illustration of such an adaptation. As in the desert and savanna, nests must be located on or close to the ground. Land birds are generally poor in variety, but marine birds and shorebirds are in great numbers in re-

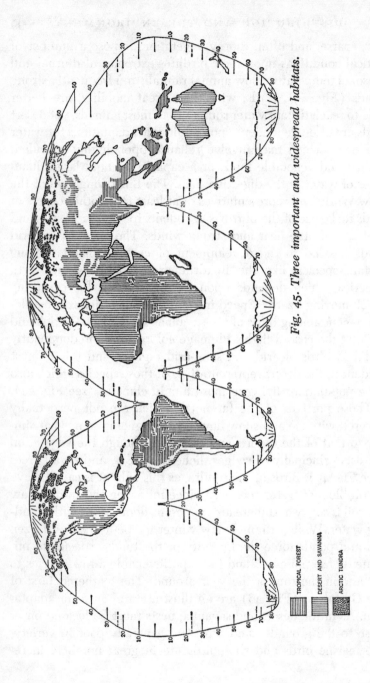

Fig. 45. *Three important and widespread habitats.*

TROPICAL FOREST

DESERT AND SAVANNA

ARCTIC TUNDRA

Fig. 46. Birds of the Arctic tundra. The Sanderling (left) feeds on the rich insect life during the summer; the Gyrfalcon (center) often remains in the tundra even in the winter when its white plumage helps to conceal it from the birds and lemmings upon which it preys. The Lapland Longspur (right) is one of the few song birds that nests in the Arctic.

sponse to the abundance of fish, insects, and other aquatic invertebrates. The distribution of predacious birds of the tundra, like the Snowy Owl, is largely governed by the distribution and abundance of their prey species. Predation pressure, coupled with lack of escape cover, has placed a survival premium on those prey species, like the Snow Bunting and ptarmigan, that have evolved seasonal changes in plumage coloration that tend to match pronounced seasonal changes in the prevailing colors of their background. A greatly restricted nesting season and long summer days have accelerated the reproductive cycle in most species, necessitating adjustments in reproductive physiology, feeding behavior, and the molting process.

The deciduous forests of temperate portions of eastern North America, western Europe, and Asia are perhaps remnants of a more extensive forest belt that extended throughout much of the north temperate land masses during the Tertiary. This important habitat is dominated by broad-leaved trees that shed their leaves during the cold winter season. The moderately moist environment and resulting growth of vegetation, though less luxuriant than in tropical forests, provides a greater number of ecological niches than the desert, savanna, or tundra. Nests can be located at every level from the ground to the top of the forest canopy, or can be concealed within the trunks and limbs of the trees, and are often of a highly specialized form or composition which could not be duplicated in other communities. The Ovenbird, a wood warbler of the North American deciduous forest, builds a domed, oven-shaped nest out of the fallen leaves on the forest floor. The variety and prevalence of food and protective shelter are additional reasons for the comparatively rich avifauna of the deciduous forest in summer. During the unfavorable winter season most of the birds of this forest community migrate to more southerly climates. Migration is an essential adaptation of highly insectivorous birds like the Yellow-billed Cuckoo and the Red-eyed Vireo, while there are some species of woodpeckers and titmice that are able to obtain the dormant, over-wintering forms of insects or even alter their diet to include dried fruits and seeds. There are often special adaptations for gathering food and getting about within this arboreal environment, which no doubt influence distribution. Certain species of wood warblers and vireos, for example, characteristically feed by gleaning the broad-leaved foliage of the forest canopy for aphids, caterpillars, and other insect life.

The broad-leaved, evergreen forests of the tropics, characterized by a continuously high humidity and maximum climatic stability, have the richest birdlife of all of the major types of habitat in terms of variety of species (see Fig. 45). Here, there are no problems of water economy, winter cold, or lack of food. The tropical rain forest far exceeds the forests of temperate latitudes in the variety of ecological niches that are available. The birds of the rain forest appear to be more specialized in their habits and occupy narrower niches within the community.

—e.g., they feed upon a single type of food plant, or nest only within a certain type of epiphyte or air plant. Consequently, though the variety of species is great, the number of individuals of a given species is limited by the narrowness of the niche to which it is ecologically restricted. Certain species of parrots, hornbills, and toucans that feed largely upon forest fruits, and nectar feeders among the hummingbirds of the Neotropics and the honey-eaters of the Australian Region are examples of rain forest birds.

Competition

Among the variety of ecological factors that can influence distribution, competition between individuals of the same species (intraspecific) and between different species (interspecific) for limited environmental resources is potentially of great significance, though often difficult to ascertain (Fig. 47). The

Fig. 47. The effect of competition on habitat selection. The peak of each curve represents optimum habitat conditions for any particular species; the descending arms the less desirable, marginal conditions. Strong intraspecific competition causes a population to spread out into marginal habitats, while strong interspecific competition causes each species to retreat to its optimum habitat where it is best able to meet the competition of other species. (After Svardson.)

effect of intraspecific competition is to encourage greater dispersal of individuals of a species, both geographically and in terms of the variety of habitats utilized. The success of such range dispersal will depend not only upon the ecological tolerance of the dispersing species but also upon the amount of competition engendered by overlap with other species having similar requirements and adaptations. Strong interspecific competition of this kind forces each species to retreat from the marginal areas and confine its distribution only to those habitats where it is best adapted to live. It is questionable that two species can occupy the same ecological niche indefinitely, because of inherent differences in competitive ability and reproductive potential. One will eventually displace the other. Various mechanisms have been evolved for easing competition. Territorial behavior will be discussed and interpreted in the next chapter as a means of reducing direct competition for food and mates between individuals of the same species. Some species having extensive geographical ranges, like the Song Sparrow (see Fig. 22), have reduced intraspecific competition by means of a remarkable diversification of their ecology. Interspecific competition is minimized by increased specialization and occupation of different ecological niches, as illustrated by the rich avifauna of the tropical rain forest.

A Continuing Process

We have stressed that the distribution of birds has not been static throughout geological time and it must now be clear to the reader that even present-day ranges are undergoing continual change. A recent warming trend in the climate of the northern hemisphere has promoted remarkable northward range extensions of birds in both the Nearctic Region (Cardinal, Mockingbird, Tufted Titmouse) and the Palearctic Region (Hooded Crow, Lapwing, and European Blackbird). Catastrophic events such as severe ice storms, droughts, and the failure of food crops have been known to cause retreats of certain species, especially at the periphery of their ranges. Other species have become established in new regions as a result of fortuitous introductions by winds, rafting, or other means. In some instances it is impossible to determine the exact causal factors for a range expansion. Perhaps the most remarkable of all distributional changes in modern times has been the successful invasion of the New World by the Cattle Egret, a common heron of Spain, Africa, and Asia. Exactly how the transatlantic crossing was made, and when, is not known, but Cattle Egrets appeared in British Guiana about 1930. If the 1800-mile journey from Africa was made without the aid of anything but a strong tail wind, this represents the only known case of the successful establishment of an Old World bird, not introduced by man, on the mainland of the Americas. Subsequently the Cattle Egret prospered and spread and its northward dispersal has carried it as far as the northern United States, where it is seen annually by hundreds of grateful bird-watchers.

Man's advent on the scene has been responsible for tremendous changes in the distribution of birds. His intentional and unintentional introductions of foreign species have frequently had drastic effects upon native species. The European Starling, originally introduced locally into North America for purposes of insect control, has subsequently prospered and spread throughout much of the continent at the expense of native hole-nesting species with which it is in direct competition (such as the Eastern Bluebird, Tree Swallow, and Great Crested Flycatcher). Man's wholesale use of chemical insecticides, without sufficient prior knowledge of their potency and effect on other elements of the environment, poses a continuing and growing threat to birds. The removal or alteration of the forest, the planting of crops, and the overgrazing of natural grasslands has so disturbed the environment as to eliminate or greatly reduce the ranges of many forest and grassland birds. Drainage of swamps and marshes have had a similar effect upon water birds.

Not all of man's activities have been detrimental, however, and there are some species that are no doubt far more abundant and more widely distributed as a result of his efforts. Gardens, parks, and residential communities provide a great diversity of ecological niches and are generally conspicuously rich in birdlife. Man-made structures now provide artificial nest sites which substitute for cliffs (Cliff Swallow and Barn Swallow), hollow trees (Chimney Swift), and the bare ground (Nighthawk). Ir rigation and the planting of windbreaks have resulted in signifi cant range expansions of still other species. The future of those species that were formerly widespread but whose distribution have been dangerously reduced, as in the case of the Californi Condor and Trumpeter Swan, rests squarely with their persecu tor and his efforts to set aside suitable habitat and to provide the needed protection for maintenance of adequate breeding populations.

6 COURTSHIP AND REPRODUCTION

In March, often before the last of the winter snow has disappeared from the grassland of temperate North America and well before the fresh green shoots of the year have appeared, a male meadowlark returns from the south and advertises his arrival from the very song posts that he abandoned the previous October. Rival males soon appear and the prairies and meadows now ring with their familiar songs. No longer feeding amiably in the loose flocks so characteristic of winter, each male now confines his activities to a particular section of the grassland and all intruding meadowlarks are met at the periphery of this territory with hostile displays and a full repertoire of song. These male displays signify the onset of another breeding season, that portion of the annual cycle devoted exclusively to the propagation of the species. The series of remarkable events that follow the arrival of the male, including acquisition of an appropriate mate and the physiological and behavioral preparation for reproduction and care of the young, will be considered here. The growth and care of the young birds and the prospects for their survival are subjects that have been reserved for a final chapter. The courtship and reproduction of meadowlarks is representative of the general pattern followed by most song birds and will provide a logical basis for comparison with a number of variant patterns exhibited by other avian groups.

We noted earlier, in our discussion of migration, that the annual cycle of birds, manifested by such overt expressions as migration, reproduction, and molt, is correlated with a complex, internal cycle of physiological events regulated in part by the bird's endocrine glands and in part by certain extrinsic factors such as photoperiod. Acceleration of gonadal activity and the development of secondary sexual characters occurs as a result of increased endocrine secretions just prior to the breeding season (see Fig. 32). In the male meadowlark, the influence of these hormones induces a change in bill color from a gray-brown during the non-breeding season to a deep, blue-black during the reproductive phase of the cycle. There is also increased vocal activity: songs are delivered more frequently and throughout longer periods of the day. The yellow underparts of the plumage are displayed to greater advantage at this season, and are exhibited in characteristic postures by the male. In many birds, differences in the color or shape of certain feathers are common secondary sexual characters. The male Pennant-winged Nightjar, for example (see Fig. 31), grows a long trailing plume on each wing at the advent of each breeding season. These ornaments are displayed before the female and after mating break off near their bases. In the few species in which the female is the more aggressive sex in courtship, as in phalaropes and jacanas, the female assumes the more brightly colored plumage during the breeding season.

Territory

The defense of a particular section of grassland insures for the male meadowlark an area of several acres of suitable habitat within which feeding, reproduction, and rearing of the young may be accomplished without interference from rival meadowlarks. The establishment and maintenance of the territory is achieved solely by the male and defended for a period of up to four weeks prior to the arrival of the females. This defense often involves the active aerial pursuit of a trespassing male (or female, later in the season) until the latter has been driven across the territorial boundaries. Encounters with those males occupying adjacent territories often entail prolonged posturing of both birds, in which the bill is pointed upward and the wings and tail feathers are opened and closed with great speed. Other displays involve the fluffing out of the plumage, especially the bright yellow underparts, and short jump-flights directed toward the intruder for a distance of several feet. While in his own territory, a male is likely to be dominant in these encounters, but will in turn be evicted if he wanders too far into adjoining territories. Since these displays are usually very effective in the displacement of trespassing meadowlarks and in the settlement of boundary disputes between neighboring males, actual combat among males is not common. Visual and vocal displays help to reduce such fighting and hence have definite survival value in this respect.

The territory of meadowlarks, in which courtship, nesting, and feeding normally occur, is the type commonly maintained in a great variety of birds. But territories vary greatly in size and function among different species, and these differences can

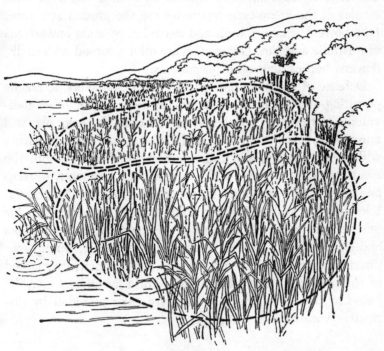

Fig. 48. Territories of two male Redwinged Blackbirds.

be correlated in some instances with differences in feeding habits and social gregariousness (Fig. 48). Birds of prey like the Golden Eagle require an area of many square miles in which to find adequate food for themselves and their young. Colonial nesting birds such as some of the swallows and oceanic birds defend only that area that can be reached while they sit on their nest, in which cases the territories may extend over but a few square inches. These birds feed in large, communal feeding areas which are not defended by individuals. The males of other species have territories which are used neither for nesting nor feeding, but consist of small arenas used solely for courtship and mating. For example, the territory of the White Bellbird is a high branch from which the male sends forth his ringing challenge to other males and his invitation to mates. This territory does not include the nest. Some of the most spectacular of the arena-type territories are the ground structures (the bowers) that are built and defended by male bowerbirds of Australia and New Guinea and are often adorned with shells, flowers, berries, and other ornaments.

Defense of the breeding territory with characteristic hostile posturing and vocalizations is usually reserved for other individuals of the same species. A male Robin, for example, will normally tolerate the presence of Catbirds and Song Sparrows within his territory, and the reciprocal is also true, with the result that the territories of the three species frequently overlap one another and are quite independent. The basis for this intolerance for members of the same species and tolerance for other species probably rests upon conspicuous plumage colors and characteristics that serve as identifying clues. But species discrimination among birds that are not distinctively marked or colored, as in many of the New World flycatchers, may be based in large measure upon auditory clues provided by distinctive vocalizations (Fig. 49).

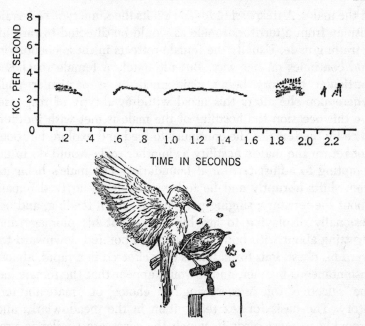

Fig. 49. A modern way of studying the sounds produced by birds involves the use of a sound spectrograph. The pitch or frequency of the sound is indicated vertically on the graph, the time or duration horizontally. Shown here are the widely differing songs of five common flycatchers: from left to right, Wied's Crested Flycatcher, Nutting Flycatcher, Olivaceous Flycatcher, Great Crested Flycatcher, and Ash-throated Flycatcher. That auditory, not visual, clues are the basis for species recognition in flycatchers is indicated by the fact that a mounted specimen of a Hermit Thrush "singing" (sound recording) like a Wied's Crested Flycatcher in the flycatcher's territory was quickly attacked by the flycatcher.

Courtship

Female meadowlarks arrive from the south two to four weeks after the males have established their territories. Though nearly identical to the males in plumage coloration and pattern, the females do not normally sing and are more unobtrusive in their behavior. As they move northward across the grasslands, feeding and exploring, they inevitably pass through the territories of the males. A trespassing female elicits the same type of hostile display from a territorial male as would be directed toward an intruding male. Usually the female retreats in these encounters and continues on her way. But ultimately a female reaches a particular territory being maintained by a particular male whereupon she alters this usual withdrawal-type of response. On this occasion the hostility of the male is met with indifference by the female. She continues to feed and explore but does not return the male's hostility as another male would do in attempting to adjust territorial boundaries. The male's behavior then shifts abruptly and he follows the newly arrived female about the territory, singing periodically, sham feeding, and occasionally displaying to her by fluffing out his plumage and strutting about with body erect and bill pointed downward toward his chest. Pair formation is thus effected in a rapid, almost instantaneous manner, and it would appear that the female has the "selective" role in exercising her "choice" of a mate and territory. The basis for sex recognition in the meadowlarks and probably in most birds in which the sexes are similar is presumably a matter of behavior. But in those species having a pronounced sexual dimorphism, differences in color or pattern of plumage no doubt serve as important sex-recognition clues.

A single male meadowlark may form a pairing bond with up to three females simultaneously. In these cases of polygyny, the male and his females feed together within the territory with little evidence of aggression toward one another. As the season progresses, the breeding cycles of the females frequently become asynchronous due to different times of arrival or nest failures, and there is little opportunity for female interactions to occur. The pairing bonds are ordinarily maintained until the females have ceased breeding, whereupon the females will wander beyond the environs of their former breeding areas without male escort and there is no revival of the pairing bond until the following spring. Though females have been known to remate with their mates of previous seasons, it seems likely that these cases of remating can be attributed to a strong "homing" instinct directed toward a particular territory, rather than to any residual or latent association between the members of a pair. Male meadowlarks frequently return to the same few acres of grassland year after year and hence rematings do occur. On the other hand, a female that returns to find her former nesting territory currently held by a new male of the same species will remain to mate with that male, even though her former mate may be present in the general area, but on an adjacent territory.

The formation of a pair bond between the sexes is an adaptation for cooperative sharing of the task of rearing the young. There are few animals other than man in which this pairing behavior has become as highly developed as among birds. Probably most birds are monogamous, unlike the meadowlarks, yet even in that type of pairing behavior the bond is usually dissolved at the end of the breeding season and is not necessarily reformed between the same individuals the following year. A lifetime pair bond has been reported for some of the geese, cranes, penguins, and hawks. In species like the Ruff, Prairie Chicken, Argus Pheasant, and Cock-of-the-Rock, there is essentially no pair bond at all, for the sexes meet only for copulation, after which the females assume all responsibilities for the nest and rearing of the young.

The formation of the pair bond, when it occurs, is usually effected on the male's territory as in the case of the meadowlarks. However, in the case of the American Goldfinch, Black-capped Chickadee, many of the ducks, and some other species that occur in social aggregations or flocks during the non-breeding season, pair formation may occur before the flock is disbanded and before the breeding territories are established. One of the outstanding features of the courtship of meadowlarks, following pair formation, is the aerial duet between members of the pair, which has its counterpart in the "sex chases" that have been reported in a number of other birds. Typically this behavior is initiated when the female flushes from where the pair is feeding or posturing. The flight that ensues may be a tortuous affair of four to five minutes duration, carrying the pair well beyond the confines of their territory. The female maintains the lead and regulates the speed of flight, while the male usually lags several feet behind except for an occasional attempt to strike his mate in midair. If the male is paired to two females, the aerial "duet" often includes both females. These aerial duets are an integral part of the daily display of courting meadowlarks and reach a peak in frequency just prior to the period of copulation.

One might ask: "Why do birds display at all?" The answer lies in the fact that reproduction in birds is not wholly a physiological process, for it requires a favorable psychological environment as well. One function of display, whether it be vocal or visual, is to provide the extrinsic stimulation needed by both of the sexes to help them through an orderly series of physiological and psychological developments, culminating in copulation (Fig. 50). Displays also play an important role in maintaining reproductive isolation between closely related species by providing clues as to the specific identity of the displaying birds.

Certain sounds that birds make, vocal and otherwise, are largely confined to the males and are most conspicuous during

Fig. 50. Mutual food begging is typical of the period of intense courtship before a pair of Laughing Gulls selects their nesting site. The subordinate posture of the female (right) suggests that the male has established the sexual dominance necessary for successful copulation.

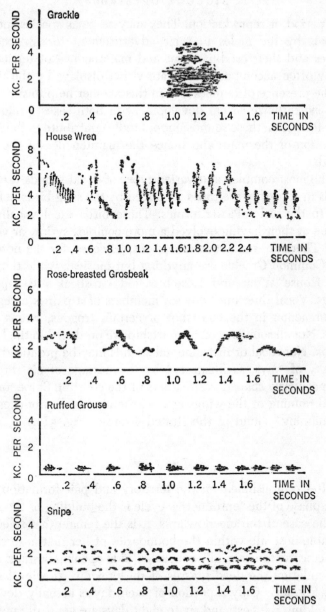

Fig. 51. *Songs and instrumental sounds used in courtship.*

the period of reproduction. They may serve as species-specific signals by the males in their advertisement for prospective mates and their establishment and maintenance of territories. They often accompany elaborate visual displays by the males in the presence of females and in this manner help to stimulate and synchronize sexual development in both sexes. Following pair formation these sounds undoubtedly contribute to the identification of the mate and hence the maintenance of the pair bond.

The most complex and varied types of vocal sounds used by birds in courtship are those produced by the song birds belonging to the order Passeriformes. These birds excel vocally by virtue of their having evolved a more complex syrinx, or voice-box. There are numerous exceptions, however, for the notes of the Common Grackle are anything but musical, while those of the House Wren and Rose-breasted Grosbeak are superior songs. Vocal duetting between members of a pair is a regular phenomenon in the courtship of certain trogons, wrens, and owls. Not all sounds used in courtship are produced in the bird's syrinx. Nonvocal or instrumental sounds may be produced in a variety of ways, as illustrated by the passage of air through the peculiarly shaped tail feathers of the courting Snipe, or the rapid fanning of the wings against the air which produces the "drumming" sound of the Ruffed Grouse (Fig. 51).

The Nest

After establishment of the territory and pair formation, the next phase of the reproductive cycle is the building of the nest. In the case of the meadowlarks, it is the female that selects a suitable nest site within the boundaries of her mate's territory and constructs a carefully concealed, side-opening nest, using as a foundation the dead grasses of the previous growing season (see Fig. 44). Only a portion of each day is actually devoted to building the nest, and six to eight days are generally needed for completion. The male meadowlark takes no part in these activities. The aerial duets and posturing between the sexes continue and copulation first occurs during the last few days of this period of nest building.

A bird's nest serves as a cradle for the eggs and as a temporary home for the developing young. A few birds use their nest for sleeping and shelter at other times of the year, as do woodpeckers and others that use cavities or roofed nests, but the "sleeping" nest is seldom used for raising the family. Nest-building is an outstanding example of the many complex behavior patterns characteristic of birds. The Old World weaverbirds are perhaps the most skillful nest builders of all birds, using a number of knots and hitches to attach the nest fibers to the support (Fig. 52). Some Old World warblers are known as tailorbirds because they stitch leaves together with plant fibers or spider silk to form a protective covering for their nests.

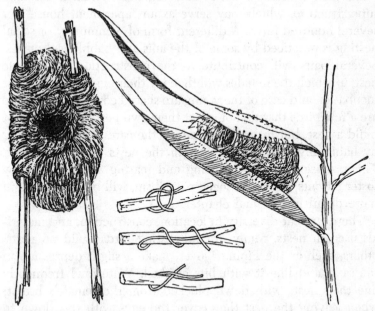

Fig. 52. Three hitches used by weaverbirds (center), the nest of an African Grosbeak Weaver (left), and the nest of an African Tailorbird (right).

Though the location of the nest, its form, and the techniques and materials required for its construction are extremely diverse among different species, the completed nest is remarkably uniform among the members of a single species. This uniformity is all the more remarkable when one realizes that many nests represent the work of young birds that have had no previous training or experience in nest construction.

The selection of the nest site and construction of the nest are performed solely by the female in many species, though in birds such as the House Wren the male may engage in some of the nest-building activity as part of his courtship behavior. In doves, penguins, and herons the male may gather the nesting material and the female constructs the nest. In some of the weaverbirds, the male does most of the nest building but the female adds the lining. In some colonial weaverbirds, the pairs build their individual nests close together within a common superstructure, which may serve as an "apartment house" for several hundred birds. A different form of community or social nesting is practiced by some of the anis and babbling thrushes. Several pairs will contribute to the construction of a single nest, in which the females will then lay their eggs. The duties of incubation and care of the young are shared communally. There are a few birds that do not select their own nest site and do not build a nest, but instead provide for the care of their offspring by habitually laying their eggs in the nests of other species. This provision for the hatching and rearing of the young by foster parents, a form of social parasitism, will be considered in more detail in the final chapter.

There is great diversity in location, construction, and materials used in nests. Many ground-nesting birds build no nests; others, such as the Piping Plover, make a slight depression in the sand and line it with bits of shell. Waterfowl frequently line their nests with down plucked from the female's breast; when leaving the nest they cover the eggs with this down to conceal them and keep them from chilling. One of the most remarkable nesting habits is that of the Fairy Tern, for in this

Fig. 53. Some types of nests. The Fairy Tern (top left), the Chimney Swift (top right), a South American ovenbird (bottom left), and the African Penduline Titmouse (bottom right).

species there is no nest in the usual sense and the single egg is laid and hatched on a bare branch. The Chimney Swift builds its nest of twigs glued together with its own sticky saliva, and affixes it to the inside wall of a chimney or, as formerly, in a hollow tree. Mud is a common nesting material of many species, used prolifically throughout as in the domed nest of a South American ovenbird or hornero, or as a lining in the case of the

American Robin. Many birds conceal their eggs from enemies by laying them in natural cavities in trees, as in the Crested Flycatcher, or by actually excavating their own nest cavity, as in the Downy Woodpecker. Other species, such as some of the kingfishers and motmots, dig nest burrows in earthen banks. Many of the smaller song birds place their nests out at the tips of small branches, where they are relatively safe from most enemies. The Blue-gray Gnatcatcher covers its nest with lichens or similar material, which provides an effective camouflage. The nest of the African Penduline Titmouse is finely woven and has a short entrance tunnel for further protection. The entrance flap on the tunnel closes by itself; the bird opens it with its foot when entering (Fig. 53).

In some species, as in the Osprey, the nest may be repaired or added to in some fashion and used by the same individuals for several years. But in general a nest is used for only one breeding season, and a new location and new materials are used in subsequent years. The cavities and burrows that have been excavated by woodpeckers and kingfishers are frequently used by other species, however, in which case new nest linings are usually introduced.

Reproduction

Reproduction in all vertebrate animals is accomplished through fertilization of an egg produced by the female of the species, but the method of fertilization and the treatment of the egg varies greatly among the different classes of vertebrates. Birds are oviparous, meaning that the eggs are expelled from the body of the female (or laid) before any appreciable development of the embryo has taken place. Oviparity, though replaced by viviparity (live-bearing) in some reptiles and in most mammals, has remained the exclusive method of reproduction in birds. The avian egg is fertilized before it is laid, through copulation as in reptiles and mammals. The sperm from the male is ordinarily introduced into the female reproductive tract by sim-

ple contact of the male and female cloacas (Fig. 54). It passes
up the oviduct and fertilizes the egg soon after the latter is released from the ovary. If fertilization does not occur, the sterile
egg may still be laid but will not develop further. During the
laying season usually one egg cell, or ovum, is released from the
ovary per day. The passage of the egg cell down the oviduct
takes 24 hours in many birds, longer in others, during which
time the egg white or albumen, shell membranes, the shell itself,
and shell pigments (not in all birds) are added through secretions from special glands in the wall of the oviduct. A hard, cal-
careous shell provides a firm support for the egg contents and
also helps to protect the embryo from desiccation. At the time

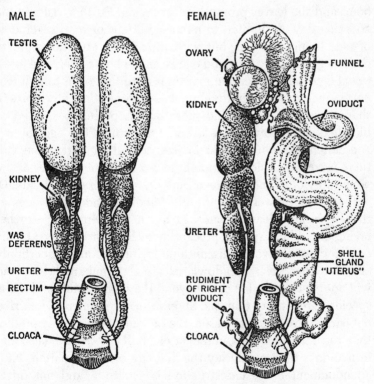

Fig. 54. Male and female reproductive tracts.

the egg is laid, the tiny embryo within is in a dormant state, no
to be aroused into further development until warmth is pro
vided.

Egg-laying in meadowlarks generally begins during the las
day or two of nest-building activity. The female meadowlar
has been participating in courtship behavior with her territoria
mate for approximately two weeks and her reproductive organs
as a result of this stimulation, have been readied for the forma
tion and delivery of the eggs into the carefully concealed nest
Just prior to and during the four- or five-day period in whicl
egg-laying occurs, courtship behavior reaches its peak and mul
tiple copulations occur. The first egg is laid just after sunrise
the female's visit to the nest is brief, perhaps less than a ha
hour, and she leaves promptly after laying. Further visits to the
nest that day are limited to minor additions or rearrangement:
of nest lining material, but with little or no attention paid to
the newly laid egg. A second egg is laid 24 hours later, and addi
tional eggs on consecutive mornings until there is a full clutch
normally four or five in number. The eggs are typically ovate ir
shape, basically white, and more or less profusely spotted o
blotched with brownish or lavender markings. The eggs of any
one clutch are quite similar in size, coloration, and shape, bu
there is considerable variation between different clutches of the
same individual and between clutches of different individuals

If a biologist were to carefully remove meadowlark eggs a:
they were laid, leaving one egg as an inducement to furthe
laying and taking special precaution to limit disturbance to the
nest, the female would discontinue laying and almost certainl
abandon that nest. Meadowlarks are determinate layers anc
will not continue to lay eggs beyond the number normal for the
species, rarely more than six. Should this experiment be carriec
out early in the nesting season, the biologist could safely predici
that the female would immediately build a second nest anc
in five days time would lay the first egg of a new clutch. Nes
abandonment or nest destruction is a natural and not infre
quent occurrence, and the females normally respond by anothe

attempt at nesting providing it does not occur too late in the season. Should the first nesting be successful, a second nest is invariably built for a second clutch, for meadowlarks are double-brooded. Repeated nest failures are known to have resulted in up to five nesting attempts (in as many nests, of course) by a single female in one breeding season.

Diversity in Eggs and Egg-laying

The diversity in size, shape, and color of birds' eggs nearly matches the diversity to be found among the birds themselves. As one might expect, egg size is more or less related to the size of the bird. Among living birds the tiny hummingbird lays the smallest egg (weighing less than a gram), while the Ostrich lays the largest. Egg size is also a function, in part, of the amount of food stored within and hence a reflection of the type and extent of parental care to be received by the developing young. Of the many shapes assumed by eggs, from the essentially spherical to the strongly elliptical, the pyriform or top-shaped eggs of cliff-dwelling birds like the murres are of special interest. Their movement would be confined to rolling in a small circle and, since there is little nest material to restrict the eggs, the survival value of such an adaptation in egg shape is at once apparent (Fig. 55). All birds' eggs have more or less brittle, limy shells, unlike reptilian eggs which are often leathery. The texture of the shell varies enormously, however, from the polished, burnished egg of the tinamous, to the rough, chalky egg of pelicans. Color and pigment pattern are normally quite uniform for each species, though variations do occur. Originally birds' eggs may have been all white, as in reptiles, but evolution has produced a great array of colors and patterns in the eggs of modern birds. Extensive pigmentation may help to conceal avian eggs from predators, whereas reptilian eggs are normally buried or otherwise hidden from view. Continuing this reasoning, it is perhaps significant that white eggs have been retained by many hole-nesting birds, as in woodpeckers and toucans, and by those birds

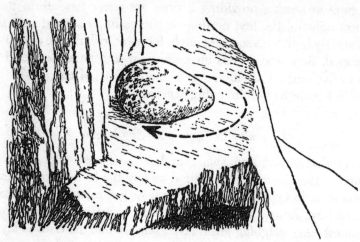

Fig. 55. The one egg the murre lays on a cliff edge is not likely to roll off.

that normally cover their eggs when they leave the nest, as in geese.

Though the interval between laying of each of the eggs of a clutch is typically 24 hours in song birds and many of the more "primitive" orders, longer laying rhythms are characteristic of many species and may extend up to four to eight days, as in the mound builders or megapodes. The full clutch—the number of eggs laid by one female in one nesting—may consist of a single egg in some species, as in certain vultures and penguins. By way of contrast, quail, pheasant, and ducks frequently have clutches of a dozen or more eggs. Clutch size is, of course, limited by the number of eggs that can be efficiently covered and warmed by the female's body. With an increase in clutch size among species there is a corresponding increase in variability in size of individual clutches, influenced to some extent by age of the female, weather, time within the breeding season, and latitude. Among populations of the same or closely related species, clutch sizes average somewhat greater in the north temperate latitudes than in the tropics, possibly in response to the greater risks that must be faced in the northern areas, such as migration or severe winters. Clutch size may be determined, through natural selection, by the number of young that a species can rear successfully without danger of underfeeding as a result of having to divide the existing food supply among too many hungry nestlings—the optimum number, in other words.

So rigid is the genetic control of clutch size in many birds (determinate layers, like meadowlarks) that experimental manipulation of the number of eggs in the nest, either by removal or addition, will not alter the female's laying of the number of eggs characteristic of her species. But some song birds, quail, woodpeckers, and others are indeterminate layers. For example, the normal clutch size of the Yellow-shafted Flicker is 6 to 8 eggs, but in one classic experiment a female was induced to lay 71 eggs in 73 days. This capacity for laying beyond a predetermined number of eggs has, of course, been artificially selected in the breeding of domestic fowl. Indeterminate layers in nature are able to replace lost or stolen eggs and thus build the clutch up to normal size. Most birds, including determinate layers, will produce a second clutch if the first attempt at nesting should fail. One clutch per season is the rule among birds of the more "primitive" orders, where the time required for incubating the eggs and caring for the young often prohibits multiple nestings. But many birds habitually produce two or more clutches in a single season. So rapid is the succession of events in the reproductive cycle in some species, as in some doves and song birds, that it is not uncommon to find a female laying eggs in a second nest while her mate is feeding the young of the first nesting. Such variation between species in the number of clutches and consequently the number of young that are normally produced during one breeding season reflect fundamental differences in growth rates and prospects for survival of the young birds.

The eggs of most egg-laying animals, including those of many insects, fishes, amphibians, and reptiles, are abandoned soon after they are laid and subjected to the vicissitudes of their environment. Often the number of eggs produced by these animals is necessarily large, for losses by predation of both eggs and unprotected young are high. In contrast, birds lay comparatively few eggs and, with few exceptions, they remain with the eggs, incubate and defend them, and continue to shelter and provide for their young for a variable period of time following hatching. This emphasis on parental care in birds is due in large measure to the slow maturation of the vertebrate nervous system and of the various physiological mechanisms associated with homoiothermy. These slow developmental processes require an extended period of dependency of the young. In mammals, the only other animals with similar developmental problems, the embryos are retained within the female reproductive tract and nourishment is supplied directly by the mother. Embryonic birds receive their nourishment from food stored within the egg (yolk) and the warmth necessary for their development is provided through incubation.

Incubation and the Embryo

The female meadowlark begins incubation as soon as the last or next-to-last egg of her clutch has been laid. Her ability to transmit the warmth of her body to the developing embryos is the result of certain changes in the abdominal skin that occur only at this time and in response to endocrine stimulation. The feathers, normally utilized so effectively for retention of body heat, have been dropped from much of the abdomen. The skin in this region, now completely bared, becomes thickened and liberally supplied with blood vessels, and it is this modified skin that the female applies directly to the eggs during incubation. No such incubation or brood patch develops in the male, for he takes no part in this phase of parental care.

During the period of incubation the female meadowlark's attentiveness to her eggs overrides all other activities. She incubates all night and during most of the cooler daylight hours, for prolonged chilling will kill the developing embryos. Brief inattentive periods during the day, averaging about 10 minutes in duration, are devoted to feeding and to preening and grooming the plumage, during which time the female is usually accompanied by her mate. Attentive periods vary somewhat in response to weather, averaging longer on cloudy, rainy, or cool days and shorter on warm, sunny days. They invariably increase in duration as the development of the embryo approaches hatching time. Periodically the female rotates or changes the position of the eggs within the nest, a behavioral adaptation that prevents the embryonic membranes from adhering to the shell. She continues incubation for 13 to 14 days, until the last egg has hatched.

Some birds (owls, hawks, swifts, etc.) commence incubation with the laying of the first egg, rather than at or almost at the end of the laying period, as in meadowlarks and most other song birds. The eggs then hatch out over a period of a week or so, and the young vary in size accordingly. The length of the incubation period is determined by the rate of development of the embryo and this rate is genetically fixed within rather narrow limits for each species. Minor variations in the duration of this developmental period can be effected by environmental temperature, especially during the early stages of embryonic development, and by the degree of attentiveness of the incubating bird and hence the degree and uniformity of warmth being transferred to the eggs. Incubation periods vary in length from 11 or 12 days in some small song birds to as much as two months in the Australian Emu and the Royal Albatross. Very long incubation periods are believed to be the more primitive condition.

Both sexes share the task of incubation in many species. This is frequently the case where male and female have similar plumage. In species in which one sex is more brightly colored than the other, it is usually the less brightly colored parent that incubates, thereby reducing the probability of attracting predators to the nest. This rule also applies to the phalaropes and jacanas, in which the duller-colored males incubate exclusively. The males do all or most of the incubating in such groups as rheas, tinamous, and button-quail.

The presence of the incubation patch is a reliable criterion of incubation behavior, for it develops only at this particular stage in the annual cycle and only in those birds that actively participate in warming the eggs (Fig. 56). But not all birds develop a

Fig. 56. The Laughing Gull, seen from below, incubating its clutch of eggs. The eggs have been outlined to make them readily apparent.

typical incubation patch. Incubating ducks and geese substitute a behavioral pattern—they pull out the heavy coat of down feathers of the breast to form a warm nest lining and cover for the eggs. Gannets and penguins transfer body heat to their eggs primarily through the highly vascularized flesh of their feet.

Attentive periods at the nest during incubation vary in length from less than ten minutes in some song birds to many days without interruption in some of the larger and more primitive groups. A unique example of attentiveness at the nest is illustrated by the various species of hornbills of Africa and southern Asia. The female hornbill remains with her eggs in a tree cavity or rock crevice for the entire period of incubation (up to 40 days) and usually until the young are at least half grown. The opening to the nest is nearly sealed shut with mud, save for a slit through which the imprisoned female is fed at regular intervals by her mate. Perhaps the most extraordinary display of attentiveness is that of the male Emperor Penguin. Soon after the female lays her single egg, she departs and does not return until the chick has hatched. There is no nest and the male incubates by standing upright and holding the egg on top of his feet and within a pocket-like fold of skin of the lower abdomen. Warmth must be transferred continuously in this manner for the entire two months of incubation, for exposure to the sub-zero Antarctic air would mean certain death to the embryo. During such a period of fasting, in the long Antarctic night, it is not unusual for the male Emperor to lose one-third of its body weight. In species in which both sexes incubate,

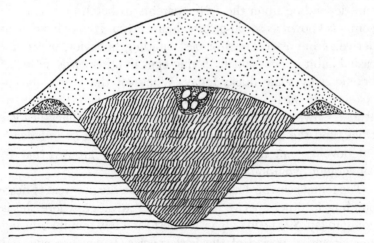

Fig. 57. A diagrammatic cross section of the mound of a Mallee Fowl of Australia. The pit contains fermenting compost, with the eggs laid in a depression on top, and the whole covered with sandy soil. (After Frith.)

there may be a regular division of labor, with one sex remaining on the nest for the same portion of each 24-hour period. The male Ostrich, for example, spends the night on the nest, the female the day.

The megapodes or mound birds of the Australian Region have completely eliminated the necessity for incubating their eggs with their own body heat. The heat required for embryonic development is instead provided by an elaboration of nest-building behavior that utilizes various natural sources of heat. Some species lay their eggs in sand, to be hatched by solar or volcanic heat. Others use mounds of decaying vegetation which they laboriously accumulate and in which they deposit and abandon their eggs (Fig. 57).

Social Parasitism

There are still other species that never incubate, but whose eggs are incubated and hatched in the nests of other birds. This practice of habitually laying eggs in the nests of other species and depending upon the foster parents to hatch and rear the young is known as social or brood parasitism. It may have been derived from a weakness of nest-building behavior, or from a casual habit of occasionally laying eggs in other birds' nests, as practiced by some ducks today. Whatever the origin, its appearance in such birds as the European Cuckoo, the Brown-headed Cowbird of North America, the Argentine Black-headed Duck, and the honey-guides of Africa, attests to its independent development in several distantly related groups, that is, convergent evolution (Fig. 58).

The female cowbird keeps close watch on the progress of nest-building in other species and knows in advance where she is going to lay. She need only visit a nest for a few minutes, during an inattentive period of the host species, to lay her egg and quickly depart. Usually no more than one or two eggs are laid in any one host nest. As many as 20 per cent of the nests of

Fig. 58. Garden Warbler feeding a young European Cuckoo.

meadowlarks may be parasitized in this manner. Other birds that frequently accept and incubate cowbird eggs along with their own clutches are various species of warblers, vireos, and sparrows. This inability of many species to recognize their own eggs is supported by the results of a number of experiments with such birds as herons and gulls, in which conspicuous alterations in coloration and even shape of the eggs did not discourage incubation (even light bulbs have been accepted). Not all species will accept cowbird parasitism, however. The Catbird has been known to throw out the foreign eggs and the little Yellow Warbler sometimes builds a new nest over one that has been parasitized. Since the time required for incubation of the cowbird egg (11 to 12 days) is frequently slightly less than that for the host's eggs, the cowbird young may hatch a day or two earlier and thus have a considerable advantage over its nest mates.

Hatching

During the few days prior to hatching, two structures reach their greatest development in the avian embryo which aid it in liberating itself from the shell. Both are transitory and disappear shortly after hatching. One of these is a tiny, horny projection at the tip of the upper bill, and is known as the "egg tooth." The other is a relatively large muscle at the back of the head and neck that provides the power needed for the egg tooth to rupture (or "pip") the shell at hatching. The emergence of the young bird from the shell is generally a laborious and time-consuming process, performed with little if any help from the parent birds, and often taking several hours in song birds and as long as several days in the larger species. The embryo breathes within the egg by means of an exchange of gases between the embryonic membranes lying just beneath the shell and the air that passes through the porous shell, but during hatching there is an important changeover of systems used in this process of respiration. The lungs begin to function for the first time and the initial attempts at filling them with air may give rise to the young bird's first vocalizations, from within the shell. The yolk sac, from which nourishment was derived throughout embryonic development, is withdrawn into the body shortly after hatching and is soon absorbed into the intestinal wall. There is little yolk remaining and this leads to one of several problems confronting the newly hatched bird—the pressing need for food.

Altricial Birds

Birds have been categorized as being either precocial or altricial, depending upon the condition and behavior of their young at time of hatching. Altricial birds are hatched with their eyes closed, have little or no down covering, and are physically unable to leave the nest. Precocial birds are hatched with their eyes open, are covered with down feathers, and are capable of leaving the nest shortly after emergence from the eggs. There are many transitional forms that fall somewhere between these two categories, making a sharp distinction impossible in some instances, yet the categories serve a useful purpose in a discussion of modes of development and parental care in birds.

The altricial condition is illustrated by all perching birds (Passeriformes) and many of the lower orders, including woodpeckers, kingfishers, hummingbirds, parrots, pigeons, and pelicans. The development of the young meadowlark and the parental care that it receives are representative of this broad category and will be presented here in some detail.

The female meadowlark normally continues to incubate her clutch of eggs for at least 24 hours following emergence of the first young, and all eggs destined to hatch do so within this period. Broken shells, the odor of which might conceivably attract predators, are methodically removed and dropped at a considerable distance from the nest, whereas unbroken eggs that fail to hatch remain within the nest indefinitely. The newly hatched meadowlark is a blind, naked, and helpless creature. It functions essentially as a poikilotherm (cold-blooded, in the manner of its reptilian ancestors) and is completely dependent upon the warmth of the brooding female for maintenance of its high body temperature. Brooding, in fact, takes priority over feeding of the young during the first few days following hatching. Only the female broods, though the male for the first time shows some interest in her activity at the nest.

For the first four days the development of the young meadowlark largely involves a coordination of those movements associated with feeding and nutrition. Both parents bring food to the nest, though the female assumes the greater share of this responsibility. Items of food, which typically include caterpillars, grasshoppers, crickets, and other soft-bodied insects, are first crushed and softened in the bill of the parent before presentation to the young. The arrival of the parent at the nest releases a characteristic reaction in the nestling known as "gaping," wherein the head is raised and the mouth opened wide. The food is placed deep into the throat of the nestling, thus triggering a swallowing reflex. The behavior of the young determines the apportionment of the food among the occupants of a nest, for those that reach the highest and utter the loudest begging notes are the ones to be fed first. The satiated nestling falls back within the nest and refuses to swallow. Food that is not swallowed immediately is retrieved by the parent and offered to another gaping mouth. Defecation is another reflexive movement that appears during this early period of development, and frequently takes place directly after feeding. The nestling squirms about within the nest until its rump has been elevated slightly and directed toward the rim of the nest. The fecal material is enclosed within a mucous sac which facilitates its removal. Both parents contribute to nest sanitation by removing these sacs and dropping them elsewhere during their flight away from the nest.

The eyes open and feather quills appear in most of the feather tracts of the nestling's body on the fifth and sixth days of age (Fig. 59). New motor coordinations appear, such as stretching the legs and wings, preening the new feathers, and cowering in the nest when frightened. In the ensuing three days there is an even more rapid improvement in coordination, resulting in increasing restlessness among the nest occupants. The wings, now well feathered, are fluttered during the food-begging reaction. Louder call notes are rendered when the time interval between feedings becomes excessively long. The female now spends less time brooding her young, for their covering of feathers is nearly complete and they are able to maintain a reasonably constant body temperature. But the rate of feeding of the nestlings by the parents increases with their age and growth, accounting for a tenfold increase in the weight of the young by the tenth day of age.

In the event that their brood also includes a nestling cowbird, the adult meadowlarks care for it as though it were one of their own. Should the growth advantage of the cowbird's earlier

Fig. 59. The development of a young meadowlark, from left to right, top to bottom: egg, 2 days, 5 days, 8 days, 10 days, 13 days, 20 days.

hatching prove too great for the weaker host nestlings, the young cowbird may in fact be the sole survivor and receive the undivided attention of the "parent" birds until leaving the nest. It will likely have no social contact with other cowbirds during this developmental period. One of the great enigmas of avian biology is the explanation of how the young of nest parasites are able to recognize and mate with their own kind later in life, without the physically enforced association between parent birds and offspring that is experienced by altricial and precocial birds alike.

Young meadowlarks are ready to fledge or leave the nest on the tenth day after hatching, but may not do so until the eleventh or twelfth day. The stimulus for fledging may come from some fortuitous event such as a disturbance at the nest by a predator, or the impatient nestling may leave the nest at the approach of the parent, in its eagerness to be fed. The strongest members of the brood may fledge a day in advance of the others, though typically the nestlings leave together. At this point, however, their associations with one another as fledglings cease for they disperse in all directions from the nest and do not return.

During the first few days out of the nest the fledgling meadowlark is incapable of sustained flight and relies upon its ability to camouflage itself among the grasses to avoid detection. If pressed, however, it can run and flutter through the grass with surprising agility. The ability to make sustained flights of any distance does not develop until about the fifteenth day of age. Here, as in the development of other behavior patterns pertaining to locomotion, feeding, bathing, and drinking, there is little if any reliance upon training by the parents or other experienced birds. The parents continue to bring food to each fledgling but the rate of such feeding begins to decrease from the peak of such activity reached just prior to fledging. The fledglings move about more or less at random, though never far from where the parents are active, and make their locations known to the parents through the use of characteristic call notes. They become increasingly curious about the ground litter and constantly explore what they find there. Learning what to eat and what not to eat is largely a trial-and-error process, though food preferences are no doubt influenced a great deal by the items supplied by the parents. The movement of insects attracts immediate attention and the young soon learn to pounce and probe for them in the grass. In a matter of a few days the young bird has developed a feeding habit characteristic of all meadowlarks, i.e., the insertion of the bill into the ground, where it is spread wide to expose the litter and to lift up leaves and bits of debris that may be harboring food.

With the attainment of flight and perfection of feeding habits —by the fourth week of age—the young become completely independent of their parents. They respond to the alarm and social call notes of other meadowlarks and may come into contact with their former nest mates once again. Their wanderings now carry them well beyond the boundaries of the nesting territory where they were reared and there is no further association between parent and offspring beyond that found within the loosely formed flocks of meadowlarks that leave together in fall migration.

The length of time that the young of altricial species remain in the nest varies from as short as 8 days in some small song birds to longer than a month in larger birds such as boobies and cormorants. To some extent the location of the nest and the circumstances under which the young must fledge have an effect upon the duration of this nestling period. Nearly all birds that nest in holes or burrows, for example, are altricial and require a comparatively long period for development prior to fledging. Frequently these nest cavities face onto wide, open spaces that afford few resting places for the fledgling that is about to try its wings in sustained flight. Consequently these young must be strong for their first trial. The Cliff Swallow, for example, feeds in the air and seldom comes to the ground. The young swallows remain in their mud nests until their wings are fully grown, then fly gracefully and strongly on their first attempt. Generally speaking, the young of large species grow more slowly than those of small species. The House Wren, for example, reaches its adult weight (7 grams) in about 12 days (Fig. 60), whereas the White Pelican (11 kilograms) requires about 50 days, though both species hatch as blind, helpless young.

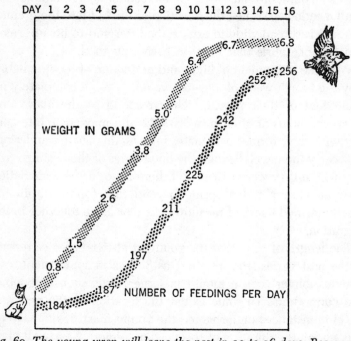

Fig. 60. *The young wren will leave the nest in 12 to 16 days. Because of its rapid growth and the great amount of proteins and minerals needed to produce its coat of feathers, the amount of food it consumes in proportion to its weight is phenomenal.*

There is no uniformity among altricial birds as to the type of food that the adults feed their dependent young or the manner in which this food is provided, no more than one finds uniformity in diet or feeding habits among the adults themselves. Insectivorous species follow a pattern similar to that described for meadowlarks, in which insects are generally crushed and softened by the parent's bill before delivery into the nestling's gullet. Some seed-eating birds feed only insects to their nestlings because of the relative difficulty with which seeds are digested. Goldfinches and other seed-eaters swallow the seeds first and then regurgitate the predigested food into the mouths of the young. Young storks are also fed predigested food, but they pick it up from the nest rim where it has been regurgitated by the adults. A young pelican inserts its entire head inside the opened mouth of the parent and deep into the gullet where shrimp and fish have been stored for it. Owls tear their prey into bits and feed their young with little pieces of flesh and entrails until the young are old enough to dismember the food themselves. A unique type of nestling food is secreted by the lining of the crop (a specialized portion of the upper digestive tract) of pigeons and doves, known as "pigeon's milk." This highly nutritious substance is fed exclusively to the young for the first few days following hatching.

In providing for nest sanitation, some altricial birds will eat the fecal sacs of their young instead of carrying them away and dropping them at some distance from the nest, as in the meadowlarks. The young of the White-rumped Swift defecate through the opening of the nest cavity, thus eliminating any problem of nest sanitation. But in other species, including the House Finch, many pigeons, and trogons, no attempt is made to maintain cleanliness in the nest, which is typically laden with fecal material and often crawling with vermin.

An intermediate category of development at hatching, which might be referred to as semi-altricial, is illustrated by nestling hawks and herons. Though these birds are confined to their nest for a period of time after hatching (the nestling period), they are covered with down and have their eyes open upon emergence from the egg and hence are somewhat more advanced in development than typical altricial birds.

Precocial Birds

Growth and parental care in precocial birds can best be illustrated here by considering the development of the chicks of the Bobwhite Quail, a bird with ground-nesting habits and an ecology similar to that of meadowlarks. A quail nest, carefully concealed in the grass at the edge of a field or in open woodland, normally will have a clutch of from 12 to 16 eggs. Both sexes participate in warming the eggs for a period of 23 days. This relatively long incubation period permits a greater development of the embryo, prior to hatching, than is the case with the shorter period characteristic of most altricial birds. During the 21st day, most of the eggs begin to "pip" and the chicks can be heard cheeping from within. About 48 hours later the first chick kicks and squirms out of its shell, with eyes open wide to the first light of day and with wet natal down plastered against its body. The muscular coordination of the chicks is such that within a matter of hours after hatching all will be led from the nest by the parents. There is essentially no nestling period for the young of precocial birds.

In spite of the advanced condition of quail chicks at hatching, their rate of post-hatching development is much slower in some respects than the relatively rapid development of some altricial young. You will recall that, by 10 days of age, meadowlarks have attained a practical degree of homoiothermy that enables them to leave their nest—no further brooding is required. Quail chicks, on the other hand, remain dependent upon their parents for body temperature regulation for a period of several weeks after hatching, a factor which contributes to a much longer bond between parents and young. During the first week, the adults may brood their young as much as three-fourths of each day, with only brief interruptions for exercise and feeding. The brooding adult merely fluffs out the feathers of its underparts, enabling the chicks to gather beneath it and absorb the warmth of its body. From the very first day, however, each chick is capable of feeding itself. The parents may direct the attention of the young to certain foods, but the chicks are quite capable of selecting their own seeds, small insects, and berries, which they uncover with a scratching motion of the feet similar to that used by adults.

The quail brood moves about cautiously as it feeds, guided and held together by the soft conversational notes of the parents. In the event of a storm or sudden drop in temperature, the young are called to the parents to be brooded. When danger threatens, the chicks scatter quickly to hide until reassembled by the parents. This fear response, present in the day-old pre-cocial chicks, is not developed in the altricial meadowlarks until about the sixth day, at which time it is expressed in the form of cowering in the nest. In both quail and meadowlarks, the facility for sustained flight first appears at about two weeks of age. By the time they are a month old the young quail are potentially independent of their parents, though they generally remain together as a family unit for another month or more—further indication of the strength of the bond between parent and offspring in these precocial birds.

Young ducklings and goslings are among the most highly developed precocial birds. Little brooding is required, for they are well covered with exceptionally thick down. They are able to swim, dive, and hunt for insects and edible aquatic plants with no parental assistance. But the diet and feeding habits of some precocial birds are such that the food is captured only with a certain amount of strength and skill, requiring further growth and learning before the chick can feed itself. Grebes, for example, feed largely on fish and aquatic invertebrates which they catch by expert diving and underwater maneuvering. Grebe chicks, though covered with down and hatched with their eyes open, are not as strong as young ducklings of the same age and are more dependent upon the adults for temperature control. Much of their time, following hatching and abandonment of the nest, is spent being brooded among the feathers of the parent's back (Fig. 61). These precocial chicks are fed

Fig. 61. The Eared Grebe carries its young about on its back, thus affording warmth to its precocial young and also protection from underwater predation.

by the parents for a variable period of time after hatching, depending upon the species. Gulls and terns normally obtain their food during rather lengthy and strenuous forays over open water. The downy young, though physically capable of following their parents on land shortly after hatching, typically remain at or near the nest and have food brought to them. The contrasting colors of the parent's bill serve as both stimulus and target for the hungry chicks, for the latter usually obtain their food by picking it out of the bill of the adult bird. Rewarded by the food they receive in this manner, the chicks soon become conditioned to learning these and other characteristics of members of their species.

The most precocial of all birds are the megapodes or Australian mound birds, in which the young are independent of their parents throughout their entire development. The eggs of these unique birds, incubated by the natural heat of warm sands or decaying vegetation (see Fig. 57), contain a greater percentage of yolk than the eggs of other birds (60 per cent by weight, as compared with 35 per cent in most other precocial species and 20 per cent in most altricial species). This permits an exceptionally long incubation period—up to 70 days—and hence an advanced state of development at hatching. Megapode chicks are homoiothermic as soon as they emerge from the egg and can fly well in a matter of two or three days. Since there is no bond between parent and young, nor between the young themselves, the chicks have no need to communicate and are quite silent and secretive.

Development of Vocalizations

Precocial chicks that follow their parents, and recently fledged altricial young that have not yet achieved independence are in continual vocal contact with the parent birds, communicating such information as distress, contentment, and hunger. Voice, then, is of great importance to birds during their first few weeks of age as well as later in life (at time of territorial defense and pair formation, as we have seen in Chapter 6). Its development and maturation are as much a part of the normal growth process in young birds as are the development of homoiothermy and the acquisition of feeding behavior.

The syrinx or sound-producing organ of birds is located at the lower end of the windpipe where the latter divides to enter the lungs, not in the throat as in the case of its mammalian counterpart, the larynx. Its operation may be roughly analogous to that of a wind instrument, with syringeal membranes providing the vibration and the windpipe serving as a resonating chamber. The nature of the sound produced can be altered through tension placed upon the syringeal membranes by muscles within and attached to the syrinx. Passerine birds (belonging to the order Passeriformes and including our typical song birds) have up to seven pairs of intrinsic syringeal muscles, while the syringes of non-passerines (all other orders) lack this complexity. As one might predict, the vocalizations of the passerines as a group are more diversified and complex than those of the non-passerines, and are conveniently categorized as consisting of call notes and song.

No such division of complexity of vocal patterns exists among the non-passerines, for in these lower forms the vocalizations are all of the simple call note variety. It is significant that when non-passerines like waterfowl, quail, and pheasant are reared from artificial incubators without opportunity to hear others of their own kind, they invariably develop the calls characteristic of their own species. Until we have positive experimental proof to the contrary, we cannot eliminate the possibility that learning from experienced individuals of their own kind may play a role in refinement of certain calls. But the available evidence of the stereotypy of vocalizations among the individuals of non-passerine species is impressive.

The call notes of passerine birds appear to be as remarkably stereotyped and genetically fixed as the vocalizations of the non-passerines (Fig. 62). These simple, explosive calls are usually fully developed during the first three months of age, except for those calls dependent upon endocrine stimulation and associated with the reproductive period. Young European Blackbirds, hatched and raised individually in soundproof rooms, developed all but 3 of 15 specific calls by the end of their third week of age without benefit of aural stimulation from other birds. Certain calls, such as those used when begging for food or maintaining contact with parent birds, are normally associated only with the nestling and fledgling period. These are eliminated from the vocal repertoire of young passerines as soon as they become independent of their parents, but may contribute to the development and formation of other calls used by adult birds in somewhat different circumstances.

Most of the attention given by researchers to the develop-

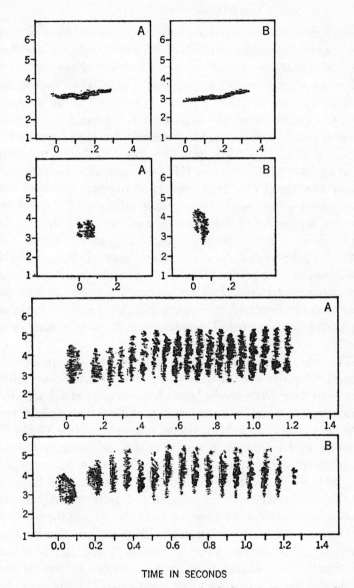

TIME IN SECONDS

Fig. 62. Call notes of the Eastern Meadowlark: (a) Experimental male, reared in isolation from other meadowlarks from 10 days of age; (b) free-living adult.

mental aspects of avian vocalizations has been focused upon the songs of passerine birds. This is understandable, for their musical quality, complexity of structure, and noticeable variability are at once attractive and challenging. The development of primary song, i.e., the song usually confined to the male and associated with courtship and territorial behavior, follows a general pattern common to all passerines that have been studied thus far (Fig. 63). Male meadowlarks first begin to render subsong, the initial phase of this development, when they are about five weeks old. This consists of random, subdued warbling, interspersed with recognizable call notes, but lacks any phrases suggestive of definitive primary song. By the first autumn there is a transition from subsong to rehearsed song, with the addition to the random warbling of distinguishable vocal patterns suggestive of the song of an adult. By the following spring the framework of random warbling and call notes has disappeared, resulting in a simplification of the total song repertoire and increased emphasis upon the primary song motifs.

The extent to which exposure to experienced individuals is essential for the normal development of primary song motifs in young song birds is a subject that has challenged scientists for centuries. It has been suggested that the more primitive type of development, as perhaps occurs among the New World flycatchers and manakins, is one in which no learning through imitation of other birds takes place, but there is no experimental proof as yet. Song birds that have been reared from the egg in soundproof rooms are capable of developing original song motifs, but these are only suggestive of the song of their respective species. These birds normally refine and supplement their own original motifs by imitating the sounds that they hear from other individuals of their own species, and this is now believed to be the general rule for most song birds. The phenomenal ability of young captive birds to imitate other birds in their artificial environment is appreciated by all bird fanciers and aviculturists. This important role of learning in normal devel-

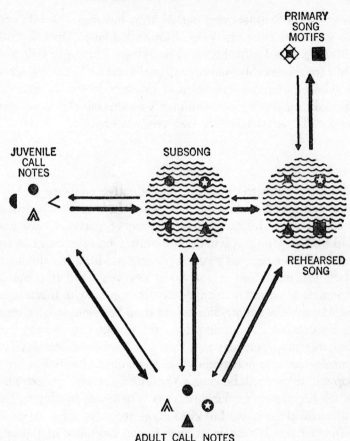

Fig. 63. Diagram of sequential development of primary song in song birds. Double arrows suggest the reversible nature of the developmental process.

opment often leads to distinct geographical dialects of primary song among populations of the same species. The period of receptivity during which learning may occur in young meadowlarks extends from the onset of subsong, at about five weeks of age, into the first winter. Meadowlarks and most other species, except those that normally mimic other birds throughout life, show a preferential receptivity to the sounds of their own species during this critical learning period, thus insuring a certain continuity of song from one generation to the next. Once learned and incorporated into the vocal repertoire, these primary song motifs are remarkably stereotyped and fixed for life. A meadowlark whose complete repertoire of primary song was recorded and analyzed during one summer was singing the same nine song motifs on its territory two years later.

Survival

We have indicated that the reproductive capacity of birds is low compared to that of most animals, and this has been correlated with the exceptional degree of parental care provided for the young. A female Bobwhite Quail can be expected to raise no more than 20 young per year; and for a female meadowlark the maximum is 10 young per year. Yet it takes no mathematical wizardry to appreciate that, even with this modest productivity, the countryside might soon be teeming with quail and meadowlarks. Assuming that each female meadowlark produces 10 young per year and that 7 of these are females (remember—they are polygynous), in the course of only five years a population of 2 will become a population of over 45,000. That no such population explosion occurs is obvious. In playing this mathematical game we failed to make requisite allowances for the many hazards that contribute to the mortality of the egg, nestling, fledgling, and adult. What are the prospects for survival in the bird's world?

The greater vulnerability of eggs and young to inclement weather and predation invariably leads to a higher mortality rate at those stages than for adults. The duration of incubation and nestling periods and the vulnerability of the nest site are additional variables often reflected in nesting success. Song birds that build open nests may have a hatching success of from 50 to 70 per cent, while hole-nesting species may successfully hatch as high as 85 per cent of their eggs. These losses can be attributed to such factors as sterility of the eggs, predation, and desertion by the parents. The last two factors continue to operate throughout the nestling period of altricial species, causing further reductions from potential productivity. Adverse weather may result in additional mortality, either directly on the young or indirectly through its effect on the availability of food. By fledging time, it is likely that only 40 to 50 per cent of the eggs laid in open nests and perhaps 60 to 75 per cent of the eggs laid in hole nests of altricial species have produced fledged young.

The first few weeks out of the nest constitute the most vulnerable period of all for both altricial and precocial young. This is the time of transition to independence. Rain and wind storms, cold weather, shortages or unavailability of food, and predation take their toll of young lives. Reasonable estimates of the survival of fledged song birds to breeding age vary from 10 to 25 per cent, with these survivors representing only 5 to 20 per cent, of the number of eggs laid.

If a young bird survives the hazards of its first year, its chances for continued survival improve considerably. The annual mortality of adult song birds may range between 40 and 60 per cent, is probably much lower in hawks and owls, herons and gulls (20 to 40 per cent), and has been reported to be less than 10 per cent in exceptional cases as in some albatrosses and penguins. It is this segment of the adult breeding population lost each year that presumably is replaced by the new increment of surviving young birds, if the population is to remain stable from year to year.

Birds seldom live to a "ripe old age" in nature. It has been estimated from analyses of banding records that most song birds that survive their first six months of life continue to survive for only one to three additional years. That some song birds are potentially capable of greater longevity, however, is borne out by exceptional individuals that have been maintained in captivity for 20 years and longer. Some species of non-passerines, including hawks, parrots, cranes, and gulls, have survived in aviaries and zoological parks for over 50 years. It is not clear, however, that these birds have a proportionally longer life expectancy in nature than do song birds. Best available estimates for the longevity of penguins, for example, indicate an average survival period of five years following the successful attainment of independence; three years for some herons, six years for oystercatchers and other shorebirds, and five years in some of the swifts. But the evidence for the longevity of wild birds is simply inadequate in most cases to enable us to make any meaningful or reliable statements, other than that the annual turnover in avian populations is undoubtedly great, perhaps greater than is commonly appreciated.

Returning to our intellectual exercise with numbers of meadowlarks, if we now provide for this normal mortality of eggs, young, and adults, we have a more realistic picture of the annual productivity required to maintain a reasonably stable breeding population. Assuming an average annual adult mortality of 45 per cent and a sex ratio of 3 males to 6 females (based on actual field studies), it is only necessary that each female contribute, on the average, 1 new individual to the breeding population of the subsequent year. This annual productivity of 1 surviving young for each breeding female may represent 10 per cent of breeding potential; any significant downward deviation from this productivity rate could conceivably affect the survival of the population. But meadowlarks are widely distributed and a temporarily lowered reproductive success in one locality is readily counterbalanced by immigration of other individuals from surrounding populations. Not so with a species that has a limited number of breeding individuals. A case in point is the plight of the Whooping Crane of North America (Fig. 64), of which there may be less than 40 surviving individuals at the present time. Though formerly widespread throughout much of the central portion of the continent, this magnificent bird is now limited to two relatively small areas, its breeding ground in Wood Buffalo Park, northern Canada, and its wintering ground in the Aransas National Wildlife Refuge on the coast of Texas. In this instance, an increase in mortality

Fig. 64. The Whooping Crane.

resulting from persecution by irresponsible hunters along the twenty-five-hundred-mile migration route, or a reduction in productivity on the breeding ground due to the encroachment of "civilization," could very well endanger the survival of the species.

APPENDIX

Common and Scientific Names
of Birds

Following is a list of the common and Latin names of the birds cited in this book. They are listed alphabetically according to their common names; the family or group name appears in Roman type, the specific or species name is italicized.

Albatross, Laysan	*Diomedea immutabilis*
Albatross, Royal	*Diomedea epomophora*
Albatross, Wandering	*Diomedea exulans*
anis	*Crotophaga*
antbirds	Formicariidae
Antcatcher, Swainson's	*Myrmeciza longipes*
Archaeopteryx	*Archaeopteryx*
Auk, Great	*Pinguinus impennis*
auklets	Alcidae
babblers	Timaliidae
barbets	Capitonidae
bee-eaters	Meropidae
Bellbird, White	*Procnias alba*
bell-magpies	Cracticidae
birds of paradise	Paradisaeidae
Blackbird, European	*Turdus merula*
Blackbird, Redwinged	*Agelaius phoeniceus*
Blackbird, Tricolored	*Agelaius tricolor*
blackbirds	Icteridae
Bluebird, Eastern	*Sialia sialis*
bluebirds, fairy	Irenidae
Bobwhite Quail	*Colinus virginianus*
boobies	Sulidae
bowerbirds	Ptilonorhynchidae
Bunting, Snow	*Plectrophenax nivalis*
Bustard, Great	*Otis tarda*
button-quail	Turnicidae

Cardinal	*Richmondena cardinalis*
Catbird	*Dumetella carolinensis*
Chickadee, Black-capped	*Parus atricapillus*
chickadees	Paridae
Chicken, Prairie	*Tympanuchus cupido*
Cock-of-the-Rock	*Rupicola*
colies	Coliidae
Condor, California	*Gymnogyps californianus*
cormorants	Phalacrocoracidae
cotingas	Cotingidae
Cowbird, Brown-headed	*Molothrus ater*
cowbirds	*Molothrus*
Crane, Whooping	*Grus americana*
cranes	Gruidae
creepers	Certhiidae
crossbills	*Loxia*
Crow, Hooded	*Corvus cornix*
Cuckoo, European	*Cuculus canorus*
Cuckoo, Yellow-billed	*Coccyzus americanus*
Diatryma	*Diatryma*
Dodo	*Raphus cucullatus*
Dove, Mourning	*Zenaidura macroura*
Duck, Black-headed	*Heteronetta atricapilla*
ducks	Anatidae
Eagle, Golden	*Aquila chrysaetos*
Egret, Cattle	*Bubulcus ibis*
elephant birds	*Aepyornis*
Emu, Australian	*Dromiceius novaehollandiae*
emus	Dromiceiidae
Finch, House	*Carpodacus mexicanus*
finches	Fringillidae
flamingos	Phoenicopteridae
Flicker, Yellow-shafted	*Colaptes auratus*

flowerpeckers	Dicaeidae
Flycatcher, Ash-throated	*Myiarchus cinerascens*
Flycatcher, Great Crested	*Myiarchus crinitus*
Flycatcher, Nutting	*Myiarchus nuttingi*
Flycatcher, Olivaceous	*Myiarchus tuberculifer*
Flycatcher, Wied's Crested	*Myiarchus tyrannulus*
flycatchers, New World (Tyrant)	Tyrannidae
frogmouths	Podargidae
gannets	Sulidae
geese	Anatidae
Gnatcatcher, Blue-gray	*Polioptila caerulea*
goatsuckers	Caprimulgidae
Goldfinch, American	*Spinus tristis*
Grackle, Common	*Quiscalus quiscula*
grackles	*Quiscalus*
Grebe, Eared	*Podiceps caspicus*
grebes	Podicipedidae
Grosbeak, Rose-breasted	*Pheucticus ludovicianus*
grosbeaks	Fringillidae
Grouse, Ruffed	*Bonasa umbellus*
guinea fowl	Numididae
Gull, California	*Larus californicus*
Gull, Laughing	*Larus atricilla*
Gyrfalcon	*Falco rusticolus*
Hawfinch	*Coccothraustes coccothraustes*
hawks	Accipitridae
herons	Ardeidae
Hesperornis	*Hesperornis*
honeycreepers	Coerebidae
honeycreepers, Hawaiian	Drepanididae
Honey-guide, Lesser	*Indicator minor*
honey-guides	Indicatoridae

hornbills	Bucerotidae
hornero	Furnariidae
Hummingbird, Bee	*Mellisuga helenae*
hummingbirds	Trochilidae
Ichthyornis	*Ichthyornis*
jacanas	Jacanidae
Jay, Blue	*Cyanocitta cristata*
Jay, Brown	*Psilorhinus morio*
Junco, Slate-colored	*Junco hyemalis*
kingfishers	Alcedinidae
kiwis	Apterygidae
Lapwing	*Vanellus vanellus*
Lark, Wood	*Lullula arborea*
larks	Alaudidae
Long Claw, Yellow-throated	*Macronyx croceus*
Longspur, Lapland	*Calcarius lapponicus*
loons	Gaviidae
lories	Psittacidae
lyre-birds	Menuridae
Mallard	*Anas platyrhynchos*
Mallee Fowl	*Leipoa ocellata*
manakins	Pipridae
Marsh Bird, Yellow-shouldered	*Agelaius thilius*
Meadowlark, Eastern	*Sturnella magna*
Meadowlark, Western	*Sturnella neglecta*
meadowlarks	*Sturnella*
megapodes	Megapodiidae
mergansers	*Mergus*
moas	Dinornithidae
Mockingbird	*Mimus polyglottos*

motmots	Momotidae
mound builders	Megapodiidae
mousebirds	Coliidae
murres	Alcidae
Nighthawk	*Chordeiles minor*
Nightjar, Pennant-winged	*Semeiophorus vexillarius*
Oilbird	*Steatornis caripensis*
orioles	Icteridae
Osprey	*Pandion haliaetus*
Ostrich	*Struthio camelus*
Ovenbird	*Seiurus aurocapillus*
ovenbirds	Furnariidae
Owl, Barn	*Tyto alba*
Owl, Burrowing	*Speotyto cunicularia*
Owl, Great Horned	*Bubo virginianus*
Owl, Snowy	*Nyctea scandiaca*
owls	Strigidae
oystercatchers	Haematopodidae
parrots	Psittacidae
partridges, bamboo	Phasianidae
Pelican, White	*Pelecanus erythrorhynchos*
pelicans	Pelecanidae
Penguin, Emperor	*Aptenodytes forsteri*
penguins	Spheniscidae
petrels (diving)	Pelecanoididae
phalaropes	Phalaropodidae
Pheasant, Argus	*Argusianus argus*
pigeons	Columbidae
pipits	Motacillidae
Plover, American Golden	*Pluvialis dominica*
Plover, Piping	*Charadrius melodus*
Plover, Ring-necked (Semipalmated)	*Charadrius semipalmatus*

Poor-will	*Phalaenoptilus nuttallii*
Ptarmigan, White-tailed	*Lagopus leucurus*
ptarmigans	Tetraonidae
puffins	Alcidae
rails	Rallidae
Redwing, European	*Turdus iliacus*
rheas	Rheidae
Roadrunner	*Geococcyx californianus*
Robin	*Turdus migratorius*
Robin, European	*Erithacus rubecula*
rollers	Coraciidae
Ruff	*Philomachus pugnax*
Sanderling	*Crocethia alba*
sand-grouse	Pteroclidae
Secretary Bird	*Sagittarius serpentarius*
Shearwater, Greater	*Puffinus gravis*
Shearwater, Manx	*Puffinus puffinus*
Shearwater, Short-tailed	*Puffinus tenuirostris*
shearwaters	Procellariidae
Shrike, Black-backed Ant	*Sakesphorus melanonotus*
Shrike, Red-backed	*Lanius collurio*
shrikes	Laniidae
skimmers	Rynchopidae
Skylark	*Alauda arvensis*
Snipe, Common	*Capella gallinago*
Sparrow, House	*Passer domesticus*
Sparrow, Song	*Melospiza melodia*
sparrows, hedge	Prunellidae
Starling, European	*Sturnus vulgaris*
sunbirds	Nectariniidae
sunbitterns	Eurypygidae
Swallow, Barn	*Hirundo rustica*
Swallow, Cliff	*Petrochelidon pyrrhonota*
Swallow, Tree	*Iridoprocne bicolor*

swallows	Hirundinidae
swallows, wood	Artamidae
Swan, Trumpeter	*Olor buccinator*
Swift, Chimney	*Chaetura pelagica*
Swift, White-rumped	*Apus pacificus*
swifts	Apodidae
Tailorbird, African	*Prinia subflava*
tailorbirds	Sylviidae
tanagers	Thraupidae
Teratornis	*Teratornis*
Tern, Fairy	*Gygis alba*
terns	Laridae
Thrush, Hermit	*Hylocichla guttata*
thrushes	Turdidae
thrushes, babbling	Timaliidae
tinamous	Tinamidae
titmice	Paridae
Titmouse, African Penduline	*Anthoscopus caroli*
Titmouse, Tufted	*Parus bicolor*
toucans	Ramphastidae
touracos	Musophagidae
Trogon, Black-tailed	*Trogon melanurus*
trogons	Trogonidae
Vireo, Red-eyed	*Vireo olivaceus*
vireos	Vireonidae
vultures (New World)	Cathartidae
Warbler, Alaska	*Phylloscopus borealis*
Warbler, Barred	*Sylvia nisoria*
Warbler, Garden	*Sylvia borin*
Warbler, Kirtland	*Dendroica kirtlandii*
Warbler, Yellow	*Dendroica petechia*
warblers, Old World	Sylviidae
warblers, wood	Parulidae

Weaver, African Grosbeak	*Amblyospiza albifrons*
weaverbirds	Ploceidae
Whitethroat, Lesser	*Sylvia curruca*
woodcock	Scolopacidae
Woodpecker, Downy	*Dendrocops pubescens*
Woodpecker, Great Black	*Dryocopus martius*
Woodpecker, Greater Spotted	*Dendrocopos major*
Woodpecker, Hairy	*Dendrocopos villosus*
Woodpecker, Ivory-billed	*Campephilus principalis*
Woodpecker, Medium Spotted	*Dendrocopos medius*
woodpeckers	Picidae
Wren, House	*Troglodytes aedon*
Wren, Long-billed Marsh	*Telmatodytes palustris*
wrens	Troglodytidae

FURTHER READING

General

Allen, Glover M. *Birds and Their Attributes.* Boston: Marshall Jones Company (1925); New York: Dover Publications (1962) (unabridged reprint).

Austin, Oliver L., Jr., and Singer, Arthur. *Birds of the World.* New York: Golden Press (1961).

Darling, Lois and Louis. *Bird.* Boston: Houghton Mifflin Company (1962).

Gilliard, E. Thomas. *Living Birds of the World.* New York: Doubleday & Company (1958).

Grassé, Pierre-P. (ed.). "Traité de zoologie: anatomie, systématique, biologie." *Oiseaux* (Paris), Vol. 15 (1950).

Heinroth, Oskar and Katharina. *The Birds.* (Translated from the German by Michael Cullen.) Ann Arbor, Mich.: University of Michigan Press (1958).

Marshall, A. J. (ed.). *Biology and Comparative Physiology of Birds,* 2 vols. New York: Academic Press (1960–61).

Pettingill, Olin S., Jr. *A Laboratory and Field Manual of Ornithology.* Third edition, revised. Minneapolis: Burgess Publishing Company (1956).

Welty, Joel Carl. *The Life of Birds.* Philadelphia: W. B. Saunders Company (1962).

Wolfson, Albert (ed.). *Recent Studies in Avian Biology.* Urbana: University of Illinois Press (1955).

Chapter 1

Colbert, Edwin H. *Evolution of the Vertebrates.* New York: John Wiley & Sons (1955).

Heilmann, Gerhard. *The Origin of Birds.* New York: D. Appleton & Company (1927).

Howard, Hildegarde. "Fossil evidence of avian evolution," *Ibis,* No. 92: pp. 1–21 (1950).

Romer, Alfred S. *Vertebrate Paleontology.* Second edition, revised. Chicago: University of Chicago Press (1945).

Simpson, G. G. *The Meaning of Evolution.* New Haven: Yale University Press (1949).

Wetmore, Alexander. *A Check-list of the Fossil and Prehistoric Birds of North America and the West Indies.* Washington, D.C.: Smithsonian Miscellaneous Collections 131, No. 5 (1956).

Wetmore, Alexander. *Birds of the Pleistocene in North America.* Washington, D.C.: Smithsonian Miscellaneous Collections 138, No. 4 (1959).

Chapter 2

Horton-Smith, C. *The Flight of Birds.* London: H. F. & G. Witherby, Ltd. (1938).

Storer, J. H. "The Flight of Birds Analyzed Through Slow-motion Photography." Bloomfield Hills, Mich.: Cranbrook Institute of Science *Bulletin* No. 28 (1948).

Sturkie, Paul D. *Avian Physiology.* Ithaca, N.Y.: Comstock Publishing Associates (1954).

Chapter 3

American Ornithologists' Union. *Check-list of North American Birds.* Fifth edition. Baltimore: American Ornithologists' Union (1957).

Cott, H. B. *Adaptive Coloration in Animals.* New York: Oxford University Press (1940).

Dobzhansky, Theodore. *Genetics and the Origin of Species.* Third edition, revised. New York: Columbia University Press (1951).

XV International Congress of Zoology. *International Code of Zoological Nomenclature.* London: International Trust for Zoological Nomenclature (1961).

Mayr, Ernst, Linsley, E. G., and Usinger, R. L. *Methods and Principles of Systematic Zoology.* New York: McGraw-Hill Book Co. (1953).

Mayr, Ernst, and Amadon, D. "A classification of recent birds," *American Museum Novitates,* No. 1496 (April 2, 1951).

Savile, D. B. O. "Adaptive evolution in the avian wing," *Evolution,* No. 11, pp. 212–24 (1957).

Wallace, Bruce and Srb, Adrian. *Adaptation.* Englewood Cliffs, N.J.: Prentice-Hall (1961).

Wetmore, Alexander. *A Classification for the Birds of the World.* Washington, D.C.: Smithsonian Miscellaneous Collections 139, No. 11 (1960).

Chapter 4

Dorst, Jean. *The Migrations of Birds.* London: William Heinemann, Ltd. (1962).

Drury, W. H., Jr., Nisbet, I. C. T., and Richardson, R. E. "The migration of 'angels,'" *Natural History* (October 1961).

Lincoln, F. C. *Migration of Birds.* U. S. Fish and Wildlife Service (Washington, D.C.: U. S. Government Printing Office), No. 16, pp. 1–102 (1950).

Long Island Biological Association. "Biological clocks," *Cold Spring Harbor Symposia on Quantitative Biology,* Vol. 25 (1960).

Matthews, G. V. T. *Bird Navigation.* London: Cambridge University Press (1955).

Sauer, E. G. F. "Celestial navigation by birds," *Scientific American,* August 1958, pp. 42–47.

Chapter 5

Allee, W. C. and Schmidt, Karl P. (eds.). *Ecological Animal Geography,* by Richard Hesse (based on *Tiergeographie auf Oekologischer Grundlage*). New York: John Wiley & Sons (1951).

Beecher, William J. *Nesting Birds and the Vegetation Substrate.* Chicago: Chicago Ornithological Society (1942).

Darlington, Philip J., Jr. *Zoogeography: The Geographical Distribution of Animals.* New York: John Wiley & Sons (1957).

Kendeigh, S. Charles. *Animal Ecology.* Englewood Cliffs, N.J.: Prentice-Hall (1961).

Klopfer, Peter H. *Behavioral Aspects of Ecology.* Englewood Cliffs, N.J.: Prentice-Hall (1962).

Mayr, Ernst. "History of the North American bird fauna," *Wilson Bulletin,* Vol. 58, No. 1, pp. 1–68 (1946).

Chapter 6

Armstrong, E. A. *Bird Display and Behaviour.* London: Lindsay Drummond, Ltd. (1947).

Hinde, R. A. "The biological significance of the territories of birds," *Ibis,* No. 98, pp. 340–69 (1956).

Lorenz, K. "The companion in the bird's world," *The Auk,* No. 54, pp. 245–73 (1937).

Romanoff, A. L. and A. J. S. *The Avian Egg*. New York: John Wiley & Sons (1948).

Thorpe, W. H. *Bird-song*. London: Cambridge University Press (1961).

Tinbergen, N. *The Herring Gull's World*. London: William Collins Sons & Company, Ltd. (1953).

Chapter 7

Greenway, J. C. *Extinct and Vanishing Birds of the World*. American Committee for International Wildlife Protection, Special Publication No. 13 (1958).

Kendeigh, S. Charles. "Parental care and its evolution in birds," *Illinois Biological Monographs*, No. 22 (1952).

Lack, D. *The Natural Regulation of Animal Numbers*. New York: Oxford University Press (1954).

Lanyon, W. E., and Tavolga, W. N. (eds.). *Animal Sounds and Communications*. Washington: American Institute of Biological Sciences, No. 7 (1960). (Contains chapters on "The ontogeny of avian vocalizations" by W. E. Lanyon, and "Bird songs and mate selection" by Peter Marler.)

Nice, M. M. "Development of behavior in precocial birds," *Transactions of the Linnaean Society of New York*, Vol. 8 (1962).

Nice, M. M. "Studies in the life history of the song sparrow," *Transactions of the Linnaean Society of New York*, Vol. 6 (1943).

Thorpe, W. H. *Learning and Instinct in Animals*. Cambridge, Mass.: Harvard University Press, 1956.

INDEX

Adaptation, 36–60; body size: heaviest flying bird, 38, largest, 14, 38, smallest, 37, wing load and, 37–38; to darkness, 45–46; in feeding, 41–43; in locomotion, 38–41: feet, 39–41, 43, legs, 26, 39–40, swimming, 11, 22, 39, 40 (*see also* Flightless birds); metabolic, 44–45; migration as, 62, 63–65, 102 (*see also* Migration); plumage coloration (*see* Feathers, coloration of); radiation and convergence in, 57–60; species as experiments in, 54–55; study of, 37

Aepyornis, 14

Agelaius, classification of, 53–54, 55

Albatross, 149; homing ability of, 77; Laysan, 77; Royal, 127; Wandering, 38

Alcids: wings of, 39. *See also* Auk

Altitude in flight, 73–74

Altricial birds. *See* Young

Alula, 23, 27

Ani, 118

Antbird, 91

Antcatcher, Swainson's, 86

Aquatic birds. *See* Water birds

Archaeopteryx, 1–5; reconstruction of, 2; dating of, 5–7, 8

Arctic: birds of, 99–102; faunal regions of, 90

Aristotle, 61

Auk, 59, 93; Great, 39, 59

Australian Region, 88, 91–92, 103

Babbler, 89; babbling thrush, 118

Banding of birds, 71, 149

Barbet, 92

Barbs of feathers, 17–19, 20

Bat, 46; ears of, 35

Bee-eater, 67, 89

Bellbird, White, 110

Bell-magpie, 92

Bering Strait: as bridge, 93; migrations over, 62, 65

Bill: change in color during breeding, 108; egg tooth on, 132; functions of, 28, 30; of Hawaiian Honeycreeper, 57–59; in preening, 18, 19, 21. *See also* Feeding

Bird of paradise, 91

Blackbird, 85, 91; classification of, 52–54, 55; European, 104; Redwinged, 52, 54; Tricolored, 53

Bluebird: Eastern, 105; fairy, 90

Bobwhite Quail, brood of, 140–41, 148

Booby, 93, 137

Bowerbird, territories of, 110

Brain, 31–33, 35

Breeding. *See* Reproduction

Bristles, 19

British Isles, birds of, 87

Brood parasitism, 130–31, 134–36

Brood patch, 127

Brooding, 133, 140–41

Bucerotidae. *See* Hornbill

Bunting, Snow, 101

Bustard, Great, 38

Button-quail, 128

Camouflage: of nests, 120; plumage as, 46–49

Cardinal, 104

Catbird, 110, 131

Cenozoic Age, birds in, 9–12

Cerebellum, 32, 35

E44

M